FOOD HEALS

Physical, Emotional & Spiritual Stories to Nourish Your Soul and Transform Your Health

ALLISON MELODY

Mike,
Cheers to health!
your good
♡ xoxo,
Allison Melody

FoodHealsNation.com

Author: Allison Melody

Title: *Food Heals: Physical, Emotional & Spiritual Stories to Nourish Your Soul and Transform Your Health*

Printed:
In the United States of America

First Edition:
November 2019

ISBN-13:
978-1-7342266-1-4 (Kindle)
978-1-7342266-0-7 (Paperback)

Imprint:
Melody Productions

Published in partnership with Laura Petersen (LaptopLaura.com), Founder of Copy That Pops (CopyThatPops.com)

Cover Photo Credit:
Jeff Skeirik of Rawtographer.com

Dedication

This book is dedicated to my parents, Pat and Lee.

Praise for *Food Heals*

"Stories of healing, like those shared in **Food Heals**, give hope and encourage the reader to tap into their own personal strength. If you are seeking to thrive in your life, not simply survive, you will find **Food Heals** to be a great source of inspiration!"

Elissa Goodman — Holistic Nutritionist & Author of *Cancer Hacks*
@ElissaGoodman

"**Food Heals** uses the power of personal storytelling to share lessons in health, wellness, and life. Allison's work with **Food Heals** will help readers connect, learn, and discover. This book inspires hope that no matter what you are going through — healing is possible and what you eat most certainly does matter!"

Kathy Patalsky — Founder of Finding Vegan & Author of *Healthy Happy Vegan Kitchen*
@KathyPatalsky

"With her Chelsea Handler-like quick wit, Allison takes her pain and turns it into her purpose. With a little humor and a lot of healing tools, **Food Heals** will truly change the way you think about health."

Jordan Harbinger — Journalist, Radio Personality & Host of *The Jordan Harbinger Show*
@JordanHarbinger

"**Food Heals** is an excellent guide for healing your body, mind, and soul. Read it and feel empowered to move forward in every way!"

Kathy Freston — Wellness Activist & *New York Times* Bestselling Author
@KathyFreston

"**Food Heals** is an inspiring book with a simple message: food matters. You'll feel motivated by the stories proving that nutrition can be the key to transforming your life for the better. If you are looking for inspiration, motivation, and education around natural health, look no further!"

Erica Mandy — Broadcast Journalist & Host of *The NewsWorthy*
@EricaMandyNews

"*Food Heals* brings together healing stories from across the world into an easy-to-understand, relatable book. While we are all different and unique, there is an underlying connection and shared experience between us that is so beautiful, complex, and deep. Allison captures those stories in this book and reminds us that no matter our health challenges, we are not alone and we can heal ourselves — body, mind, and spirit!"

Katie Krimitsos — Producer & Host of *Women's Meditation Network*
@Womens.Meditation.Network

"Allison is truly creating a food revolution with her books, podcasts, and films. *Food Heals* will change everything you think you know about healing."

Kerri Kasem — TV Personality, Radio Host & Wellness Expert
@KerriKasem

"With this book, Allison continues to set the wellness world on fire."

John Lee Dumas & Kate Erickson — Founders of *Entrepreneurs On Fire*
@JohnLeeDumas & @KateIErickson

"Allison is the go-to-girl for healing yourself — mind, body, and spirit. *Food Heals* offers uplifting stories, candid conversations, and practical real-world insight to inspire you to move past the indecision, the guilt, the fear…and instead, move into a life beyond what you ever thought possible! Seriously, a must-have for your life!"

Danielle Mercurio — Speaker, Confidence Coach & Host of *The Danielle Mercurio Show*
@DanielleMercurio

"Losing your parents at an early age can be earth shattering — I can attest from personal experience. In *Food Heals*, Allison shows us that your biggest trauma can lead to your biggest triumph as she takes us on her journey from losing everything to rebuilding her life with candor and style."

Michael O'Neal — Host of *Solopreneur Hour*
@SoloHour

Table of Contents

CHAPTER 1 – ALLISON MELODY: TURNING PAIN INTO PURPOSE & TRAUMA INTO TRIUMPH

Turning Pain Into Purpose & Trauma Into Triumph

By: Allison Melody

Filed Under:
#foodheals #loveheals #thejourneyheals

My hair was wild, my feet were muddy, and my smile was contagious. After playing in the creek for hours, my pastel pink pants would turn a dark shade of maroon and my Keds would be soaking wet.

I was 10 years old and determined to leave clean but come home dirty (much to my parents' chagrin).

Life was good for this only child who could do no wrong.

My parents were madly in love and I never saw them argue. They had met in the 70s in Chapel Hill at The University of North Carolina where my mom was in graduate school and my dad was an undergrad.

My mom always said it was love at first sight.

They got married in a whirlwind romance and had little 'ole me at the dawn of a new decade in December of 1980.

Growing up, the house that my dad built on Lake Ellen Drive was the gathering place for my friends and the neighborhood kids. My parents opened their doors and their hearts to anyone who needed them.

Our home was situated between a lake and a creek with a freakin waterfall connecting them. (Seriously, I did not realize how rad this was until I got older!).

My friends and I would climb the rocks and trees, play tag, and run around reckless and free. Ending up back home and exhausted after a hard day of play, my parents would whip up something in the kitchen for us to enjoy. (My dad's potato pancake game was on point!)

Life was a dream. The only hardship I faced was finding matching clean socks and trying to get home before the street lamps went dark.

As I got older, there were fishing trips, boat rides, and UNC football games. Sleepovers, pool parties, riding our bikes, and counting down the days until we turned Sweet 16.

Our theme song was Deanna Carter's "Strawberry Wine" and the TV show, *Dawson's Creek* seemed to be modeled after our lives. Movies, sneaking in and out of each other's windows, and teenage heartache was the name of the game. Yes, Capeside's fictional faves seemed to be perfectly modeled after my Chapel Hill up-bringing.

I was a happy girl, blissfully unaware of stress, pain, or trauma.

How quickly this happy girl would lose her innocence and childlike wonder.

When it was time for me to head to college, I chose UNC Wilmington, a two-hour drive from my hometown. At the same time, my parents uprooted their lives and moved to Topsail Island — where they owned a beach house — in order to start fresh and be closer to me. Topsail was just 30 minutes from my dorm.

My father had started what would become a highly successful and lucrative law practice in their new beachfront community, while my mom spent her days tending to the house, playing with the dog, and watching the waves from her beachfront chair.

I visited them a few times a month in between classes, working toward my film degree and dreaming of my future illustrious movie career in Hollywood. Wilmington had a booming film industry at that time, so I was on movie and TV sets whenever I wasn't in class.

I even got a couple cameos on *Dawson's Creek,* the show that emulated my childhood! My dreams seemed well on their way to coming true.

But life is what happens to us while we are busy making other plans.

My World Collapses

The word *cancer* had never entered my vocabulary before. It was something that happened to other people. People I didn't know.

So when I drove the commute from my college apartment to see my parents one sunny afternoon during my junior year of college, I had no idea the bombshell that was coming. My dad had asked me to meet him at his office.

"Mom has cancer."

I didn't know what shock was, but in this moment I just went numb.

How could this be?

We drove back to the house, and I sat with my mom and dad. They said, "It's okay to cry."

But I didn't. *I was strong*.

I was numb.

Just a junior in college, I learned that my mother (and best friend) had only months to live.

My mom had started getting sick when I was in high school, although she hid the signs from me for years. Multiple Sclerosis is an autoimmune disease described as the immune system literally attacking itself, leaving the body vulnerable to sickness and disease.

At first, my mom felt numbness and tingling in her hands and feet, but over time, even just walking became more and more difficult. I now realized this was why she sat and watched the waves all day. She was in constant pain.

It was a struggle just to get up. Her pain was increasing quickly.

Doctor after doctor, drug after drug, nothing could ease her pain.

FOOD HEALS

Every new month brought a new specialist and a new prescription. My mother had boxes full of medications. She had to write down each drug she took throughout the day just to keep track of all the pills and not to overdose.

And each drug introduced at least three new side effects. The more drugs she took, the worse her condition seemed to become.

"Curing" my mom's cancer became my family's full-time job. But no doctor and no test could determine the cause, and therefore, no doctor and no test could determine the best treatment.

We sought the best care in the state. UNC. Duke. Specialists. World-renowned oncologists.

Still no clear answers.

What followed over the next few months were weekly chemotherapy treatments. How quickly my mother lost her gorgeous head of hair! Her skin began sagging, she lost way too much weight, and she started growing hair in all the wrong places.

I wondered, "Is all this making her healthier or sicker?"

But doctors assured us that this was our only option. And since doctors are "God," well, you know, we soldiered on.

But things just got worse.

"Does nutrition matter?" I asked one day to Dr. God.

"No. It does not matter. Your mom can eat anything she wants."

Thank you, Dr. God. Whatever you say! Blessed be the fruit?

When they moved her from the hospital to hospice care, I was told it was only temporary.

I didn't know that hospice is where they take you to die.

I hung out in her room each day, studying and reading as she slipped away a little more, further and further into a catatonic state.

I don't remember our last words because I truly did not comprehend the gravity of the situation.

Denial.

One month before my college graduation, my mother, the beautiful Patricia Ann Doughty Biggar, took her final breath.

I had left to pick up my great aunt from the airport who had come into town to visit. When I arrived back at the hospice, my father and boyfriend met us in the lobby.

"She's gone."

That was the day I finally cried.

My mother's death hit my father hard too. His soul mate, his best friend, his reason for living was now gone, and no one could explain why.

But, my dad and I were determined to make it through. We had each other. It was us against the world. And we were going to be okay.

Hollywood, Here I Come

After graduating with a Film degree, my dad supported my idea of moving to California to pursue a filmmaking career in Hollywood. I dreamed of making big budget films and popular TV shows.

But, as is usually the case, fate had other plans.

You may not know this, but when you cross the state line and enter into California, they pull you over, strap a yoga mat onto your back, and put a green juice in your hand. (Kidding, sort of).

In Los Angeles, I began meeting people. People with incredible healing stories to share.

I met a woman who healed herself of ovarian cancer through a raw vegan diet and healing her emotional trauma.

I met a man who reversed his autoimmune condition and lost 100 pounds by green-juicing his way back to health.

FOOD HEALS

I met another woman who healed cervical cancer through a raw food diet, meditation, and kundalini yoga.

I was learning about acupuncture, vitamin C therapy, plant-based diets, cryotherapy, intermittent fasting, myers' cocktails, alkaline diets, functional medicine testing, juice-fasting, and ozone therapy: all of these crazy alternative modalities of healing that were foreign concepts to me and my Southern roots.

I started making connections.

"The body can heal itself if given the tools it needs to do so."

"Food has the ability to harm us or heal us!"

OMG, *Food Heals!*

As you read this, you might be thinking, cue 90's valley girl accent, *"Well, duh!"* But, at the time, this information was completely *revolutionary* to me.

The lightbulb had gone off, and I was ready to shout my new-found knowledge from the damn rooftops!

I had started a film production company, and somehow every single one of my clients was health and wellness related. Every person I met in LA and every person I worked with solidified my beliefs. I knew that I was going to dedicate my life to holistic health and healing. I knew I wanted to educate and inform people on how to prevent and reverse disease.

That was 2006. And I was almost as blissed-out and innocent as I was in that childhood memory I shared at the beginning of my story.

But then, WHAM.

The Universe had another shitstorm in store for me.

No, Not Again

Two years after my mom died, and only months after my dad remarried, I got a call from my father. I'll never forget his words.

"I'm sick, Baby. It's bad. Come home."

I flew directly home. I promised my dad that I would save him. I told him he had to taper down the massive amounts of pharmaceutical drugs and drastically change his diet. He agreed to try.

We visited a holistic doctor who said he could help my father if we let him.

This new doctor's office was in his home, not in a medical center. It smelled like incense, not medicine. He wore a flannel shirt, not a white coat.

I could see the judgment in my dad's eyes.

NOTE TO HOLISTIC DOCTORS: *Please put on a white coat and don't smell like patchouli. A stethoscope wouldn't hurt either. This way people like my dad and other baby boomers might take you seriously.*

(Okay, rant over ;)).

This holistic MD had assisted thousands of stage 4 cancer patients in making full recoveries. My dad's illness did not have to be terminal.

But my dad chose not to change because he did not believe it would help. He did not stop the pharmaceutical drugs, he did not alter his diet, he did not change his unhealthy habits.

The same oncologist who treated my mother prescribed my father more drugs, more chemotherapy, and more radiation.

The same doctor who treated my mom told me, "Go home and let him die."

I pleaded, I begged, I cried.

"Dad, drink this green juice! It will heal you!"

Eat garlic cloves! No sugar! No processed food! Do yoga! Meditate!

My dad lovingly laughed as he sipped his whiskey and smoked his cigar.

No way. My dad was going to live his life *his way*.

And I? I had to let him die, *his way.*

The hardest thing I have ever had to do in my entire life was to accept my father's decision.

To stop making smoothies and start listening. To let him be himself and not push my new-found beliefs on him.

I lost both my parents to cancer by the time I was 25 years old.

My Story Begins

There wasn't enough green juice in the world that was gonna get me through this. (And by green juice I mean red wine. But, you knew that, right?)

I had to grow up fast and figure life the f**k out.

As devastating as this tragedy was, it instilled in me an innate sense of my purpose in the world. My mission is to awaken people — those who want to listen — to the fact that a healing miracle is always possible.

So, now you're likely thinking, "Okay, this is the end of the story. Now Alli goes on to live out her mission, help people, and write this book. Blah, blah, blah."

Actually, I'd say this is where my story begins.

Because now, after losing both my parents, I had to start the long process of healing. Not only had I lost these two incredible people, but I also lost my stability, my trust in life, and that feeling that everything was going to be okay.

Everything was utterly shattered.

I now lived in constant fear. Fear that I would get sick too. Fear that I would run out of money.

Fear that I would die.

I was 25 years old, and it felt like the weight of the world was on my shoulders. This is when the 'school of life' finally began for me. Nothing I was taught in high school, college, or by my parents could have prepared me for it.

Not only did I lose the only family I had ever known, but I also found out I was robbed and broke. The executrix of my father's estate had completely mismanaged it and stopped running his business efficiently. In addition, the money supposed to be paying the mortgages on his investment properties was suddenly nowhere to be found.

Someone from Bank of America called me and said, "You're losing thousands of dollars a day. Mortgages haven't been paid in months. Your homes are in foreclosure."

I literally didn't know what foreclosure meant at the time.

So I retained a lawyer. "The estate is broke. It's all gone," he told me. I didn't even have the money to pay him to help.

Depression, fear, anxiety, anger.

How the hell was I going to survive?

I didn't like drugs, so I couldn't numb the pain.

I didn't have a religious background, so I didn't know how to talk to God.

Vodka helped, but only temporarily.

So, I put my faith in *food*. Greens, fruits, vegetables, nuts, beans, seeds, soups, and smoothies.

"They can't take my health away!" I declared.

"At least I will never get cancer!" I decided.

Food became the basis of my healing for a long time. By changing my diet and transitioning to plant-based foods, my body began to change. My digestion improved, my skin cleared up, I lost weight.

Health was my passion, and so it was fun to focus on being healthy and avoid being depressed.

By the time I went fully plant-powered, I was a new person. I had never felt so good in my life! But I still had dark days. So I needed to take the next step in my healing journey, emotionally.

Gratitude Becomes My Go-To

I knew nothing about the connection between our bodies and our emotions growing up. It just wasn't a part of our vernacular. Five stages of grief? What is that? I was clueless about how to get in touch with my emotions.

They say, "You gotta feel it to heal it." So, I slowly learned methods of emotional healing that would help me finally grieve.

Meditation helped me quiet my mind and halt my anxiety.

Music allowed me to feel my emotions more deeply.

Counseling allowed me to give the feelings a voice that I hadn't been able to express before.

Hypnosis allowed me to access and heal traumatic memories I had suppressed.

Slowly, I began to allow myself to grieve. And through my grief, I was able to find gratitude.

In the presence of gratitude anger, sadness, pain, anxiety, and depression couldn't exist.

And in this space, I was able to turn my pain into my purpose.

Turning Trauma Into Triumph

Along with the emotional healing came the spiritual healing. I had turned my back on religion my entire life, after having negative experiences at church — not rapey ones, thankfully, just being told I was going to hell if I wasn't 'a good girl,' and that did not resonate with me.

But throughout this journey, I began discovering the work of people like Edgar Cayce, Sylvia Brown, Marianne Williamson, and Gabrielle Bernstein.

My mom had always been on the 'woo woo' side, while my dad was straight up 'what you see is what you get.' So, for me, topics like spirituality, the after-life, and a belief in God, a higher power, or the Universe was always 50/50.

It felt like I had an angel and devil on my shoulder where the angel would say, "Dude, everything is amazing in heaven. Your parents are blissed out AF!" And the devil would retort, "Nah, they are dead and buried, and that's it!"

Over the last ten years, since the death of my father, I am happy to say that the angel won. I believe I am being guided and supported. I believe in the after-life. I believe that my trauma is something that can empower me to help others.

Now, I am not going to tell someone who has just lost a loved one or gone through some horrible trauma, "God has a plan." (I'd cut a b***h if someone had said that to me after my loss!).

But I do believe that there is life after death and that my parents are still with me, guiding me and loving me. And so in order to have a relationship with them, I had to forgive.

Forgiveness opens the door to freedom.

I had to forgive myself for not saving my parents.

I had to forgive myself so that today I can have a loving relationship with them even though they are not physically here on this planet.

Love Heals

And I'm still working on having a deeply loving relationship with *myself.*

In 2015, I started the *Food Heals Podcast*, which has been hailed as *Sex and the City* for food, y'all! This was a place for me to finally have a voice in this crazy world of health and wellness. This was a place where I could share my story along with the healing stories of others and indeed start a food revolution!

Finally, I could stop preaching to those who didn't want to hear what I had to say and speak directly to those who I could help, those who were seeking knowledge, inspiration, and motivation to get healthy.

At first, when I thought about starting my podcast, fear overwhelmed me.

Who will listen to me?

Who am I to start a podcast?

Will this even help people?

Imposter Syndrome: a disease many of us suffer from. Sound familiar?

Through my spiritual work, I had to learn never to hold back who I am. To stop playing small. That my story can help others. That everyone doesn't have to like me or agree with me. That I do not have to be a doctor to talk about health. That I am not a fraud.

It is impossible to be a fraud when you are your true self.

Today, when I feel scared about standing up for what I believe in or saying what I honestly believe, I remind myself of this powerful quote by Marianne Williamson:

> *"Our deepest fear is not that we are inadequate. Our deepest fear is that we are powerful beyond measure. It is our light, not our darkness that most frightens us.*
>
> *We ask ourselves, 'Who am I to be brilliant, gorgeous, talented, fabulous?' Actually, who are you not to be? You are a child of God. Your playing small does not serve the world. There is nothing enlightened about shrinking so that other people won't feel insecure around you.*
>
> *We are all meant to shine, as children do."*

The Purpose of This Book

That's why I am writing this book and sharing these incredible healing stories with you. When we live in our truth and stand in our power, we are unstoppable!

"Your story may be the key to unlock someone else's prison." - Instagram Meme

When we share our stories, we give others permission to share theirs as well. And collectively, we all heal.

I will continue to podcast.

I will continue to write.

I will continue to make films.

I will continue to share my story, speak my truth, and heal myself.

And I will share your stories too.

The stories that follow in this book are a testament to the healing power of our minds, bodies, and spirits. It is my deepest hope that this book inspires you to live a happy, healthy life full of vitality and longevity.

Allison Melody is an eco-entrepreneur with a passion for film, fitness, and food. As a Podcast Host, Film Producer, and International Speaker, Allison's mission is to inspire people that the body has the ability to heal itself when given the tools it needs to do so.

Allison is Host of *The Food Heals Podcast*. Being hailed as "Sex and the City for Food," *Food Heals* brings together experts in the field of nutrition, health, and healing to teach you the best-kept natural secrets to being a hotter, healthier, happier YOU!

Additionally, as a filmmaker since 2004, Allison has directed and produced documentary films, commercials, music videos, and web videos on the topics of social justice, human rights, animal rights, and public health.

In 2019, her documentary *Powered By Plants* debuted at The French Riviera Fest in Cannes, France.

With her years of experience in film production, podcasting, speaking, writing, marketing, and coaching, Allison helps successful wellness entrepreneurs build wellness empires.

As a sought-after international speaker, Allison has presented at events and conferences including The Sundance Film Festival, Vaynermedia, Podcast Movement, NAB Show, Growth Now Movement, New Media Summit, The Cannes Film Festival, High Vibe Live, We Are Podcast Australia, Podfest Expo, She Podcasts, Release What Weighs You Down, The Podcast Cruise, Transformed Live, and more.

And now, Allison is the proud author of this heartfelt book *Food Heals*, with more projects in the works.

Learn more and connect:

FoodHealsNation.com

 @AllisonMelodyTV

 @FoodHealsNation

CHAPTER 2 – WHAT IS A "FOOD HEALS" STORY?

What Is a "Food Heals" Story?

Our body has the ability to heal itself if given the right tools, and the sooner we stop outsourcing our health and start taking it into our own hands, the faster we are able to heal - mind, body, and spirit.

For me, my journey started with food. Progress here then led me down the path of emotional, spiritual, and physical healing.

For many in this book, their journey started with something else.

And for you, it may be completely different as well.

There is no single path. But we are all on the journey together.

I was inspired to create this anthology after conducting thousands of interviews as a documentary filmmaker and podcaster. Stories that have made me laugh, have made me cry, and have given me new insights into my own life.

I believe our stories are the key to unlock someone else's prison. Stories are healing, stories unite us, and stories *change* us.

A *Food Heals* story is an inspirational, true story about an extraordinary experience or moment that changed someone's life and set them down the path of health and wellness.

It is a story that opens the heart and rekindles the spirit.

Stories are personal, real, raw, and often filled with emotional, physical, and spiritual lessons.

It is my hope that these stories inspire you to live a healthy, happy radiant life.

XOXO,

Allison Melody

Filed Under

The stories that follow fall into these categories:

#alternativemedicineheals
#braveryheals
#energyheals
#exerciseheals
#foodheals
#gratitudeheals
#juiceheals
#loveheals
#meditationheals
#nutritionheals
#spiritheals
#thejourneyheals
#theuniverseheals

CHAPTER 3 – DR. STEPHEN CABRAL: YOU CAN TRANSFORM HOPELESS HEALTH STRUGGLES INTO VIBRANT LIFE AND VITALITY

You Can Transform Hopeless Health Struggles into Vibrant Life and Vitality

By: Dr. Stephen Cabral

Filed Under:
#foodheals #nutritionheals #alternativemedicineheals

"We can't help you anymore."

That's not what any teenager wants to hear from their doctor when they're feeling physically defeated and desperate for help.

My immune system was shot and I had zero energy. My glands were swollen, my stomach was bloated and my skin was inflamed. I'd seen over 50 different doctors, tried over 100 different treatment protocols, and there was still no hope of recovery.

It all started innocently enough with some persistent acne. That sounds benign, right? I mean, pimples are something of a rite of passage as a teenager.

Acne is not supposed to be a life-altering diagnosis.

And the solution seemed easy at first. My mother took me to a dermatologist where the doctor looked at my skin under a bright light. Then they handed me a prescription for an antibiotic and some cream.

That's it - you're on your way. No big deal!

That is until the "cure" became the "disease." That's where my health crisis began. And it went significantly downhill from there.

I was put on antibiotics for three years to keep acne at bay, which meant that by the age of 17, I had taken over 3,000 amoxicillin pills!

It wiped out my gut.

FOOD HEALS

It wiped out my immune system.

The pills made me sicker - not better.

The doctors just shrugged their shoulders and sent me home, saying there wasn't anything else they could do.

I was just a kid!

Everything hurt - my joints, my gut, my brain - everything. I was a mess.

I was finally diagnosed with Addison's disease, Type 2 Diabetes, fibromyalgia, and an autoimmune condition. There didn't seem to be anything that wasn't wrong with me.

And they told me that there was no hope. They looked at me and said, "You just need to learn to live with the symptoms."

I was shocked and frustrated. How could this be?

But little did I know that this personal nightmare was about to turn into my life's work. But I'm getting ahead of myself here.

Let's go back a little.

When I was dealing with these illnesses, no one believed I could improve. I would get a tiny bit better, and then I would relapse. A small bit better, and relapse again.

But I was just so stubborn. And I saw people like me who were getting better, so I tried to copy what they did. It wasn't perfect. But I started to take tiny steps forward with my health.

And this is when my life started to turn around.

I met an "alternative" health doctor who explained to me how I got to where I was and how I could become well again. That's when I began my recovery process and learned, finally, why my health had taken such a downturn.

Western medicine only treats the symptoms. It doesn't address the underlying issues.

So my doctors were treating my chronic symptom of acne, but they weren't addressing the chronic inflammation and root cause imbalances that created the symptoms.

And their treatment actually caused further imbalances, just making me sicker. I was in a downward spiral. My body was in a nosedive of inflammation. Western medicine doctors and specialists didn't know how to pull me out.

But, my new alternative medicine practitioner started to teach me about my body. And I learned some amazing things that helped me start to help myself feel better.

I started to heal myself!

Heal myself? This was shocking to say out loud at first because I'd always been taught that it was the doctors who would heal me.

But I learned that when it comes to chronic disease, a good doctor doesn't actually heal you. Their job is to help you determine what your body needs and allow the body to do its job - heal itself!

I couldn't wait for someone else anymore. My health was ultimately in my hands.

What a relief. Once I gave my body the chance, it was fully capable of getting itself back into balance. This breakthrough changed everything.

I started healing my dis-ease. I reduced my chronic stress. And I repaired my gut.

I started to feel better. I started to live better. And my chronic health problems ceased to be problems altogether.

I became passionate about Functional Medicine Detoxing because I saw the difference it made in just a short time period. I nourished my body with all those phytonutrients from plants. I felt satiated. And I didn't even go after coffee because I was so energized.

My experience taught me that you really can heal in 12 to 16 weeks. All the red blood cells in your body turn over every 90 to 120 days. So, a true detox can give you a fresh start.

FOOD HEALS

As you repair your health, your mitochondria become replenished. You'll have more nutrients in each of the cells. You're literally regenerating the body!

Hope isn't lost.

You just need to start address what your individual body needs.

And like me, you need to learn to address stress. Our mental and emotional health is a piece of our total health puzzle, although it's so easy to overlook.

I had been suffering from constant stress, but didn't see that as related to my physical problems.

Some people can't heal their bodies until they overcome some emotional-based trauma. It affects your hormones. It affects the nervous system. Then, it affects your immune system.

And you can't truly heal until you work on the whole person.

At a young age, once I learned the true path to healing, I decided my life would be dedicated to helping others through the process of healing their bodies and minds to renew their health too.

I didn't set out to be a Doctor of Naturopathy and Integrative Health Practitioner. It became my calling.

Now, after almost 20 years and over 250,000 wellness client appointments, I am confident that anyone can take back control of their body and their life.

I have studied, worked, and lived in clinics all around the world. This intimate setting allowed me to talk in depth with the patients at these clinics and listen to their struggles and path to wellness. I got to see first-hand the remarkable recoveries these people were making.

It is now my mission to take all forms of medicine from around the world and combine them into one healing practice.

I want people to understand that they can transform their bodies. When people see they can take control of their health, they really do it. They just need to believe it can work for them and they need to believe that change can happen.

My mission is to get this information out to everyone needlessly suffering, stuck in a nosedive with their health, and feeling there is no way out.

Your body knows the way out.

You just have to open the door.

You just have to find out what the underlying imbalances are that keep you from achieving the energy, mood, health, and quality of life you need to live longer and stronger. Because the downside is that if you do not optimize your health, the likelihood that you'll live as long as you should greatly decreases!

This isn't just my story.

Thousands of others have changed their health from a state of chronic sickness, pain, weight gain, depression, and suffering to one of energy, vitality, and happiness.

Life can continue to get better every year!

I think of my own case — because it shouldn't happen like this — but each year older I get, my health actually improves. I'm stronger and more vibrant now, over 20 years after first getting sick at age 17!

The doctors had me convinced my life was lost. But they were wrong.

And if you've given up on yourself, you might be wrong too.

The time is now.

I believe that by changing your body, you can change your life. And when this happens you will have the energy, vitality, and zest for life you've been searching for.

You can be, do, learn, and have anything you want in life – it's just up to you to take that first step. And this all starts with changing the body you're living in.

You can transform hopeless health struggles into vibrant life and vitality!

You are full of potential.

Your life can be everything you want it to be.

And your amazing body has the wisdom to heal itself.

I wish you all the best life has to offer and Ayubowan.

Dr. Stephen Cabral is a Board Certified Naturopathic Doctor with post-doctoral specialties in Ayurvedic and Functional Medicine.

He also runs one of the largest health and wellness practices in the U.S. and where he and his team have completed more than 250,000 client appointments.

Dr. Cabral is the founder of the Cabral Wellness Institute and StephenCabral.com.

Food Heals Podcast **Episodes 201 & 286**

CHAPTER 4 – ABBY PHON: IF I CAN HEAL MYSELF, SO CAN YOU!

If I Can Heal Myself, So Can You!

By: Abby Phon

Filed Under:
#foodheals #loveheals #alternativemedicineheals

Things should have been perfect.

In the space of a few short years, I had graduated with honors from New York University's Tisch School of the Arts, married the man of my dreams, moved into a stunning building in New York City, and was pursuing my dream of becoming an actress.

But there was one thing keeping me from really enjoying life. Every day I felt worse and worse - unwell, sick, and in pain.

I went to what felt like 300 traditional doctors in search of an answer. Not one of them could figure out what was wrong with me. Out of frustration and desperation, I decided to take matters (my health!) into my own hands.

I took a chance and went the non-conventional route (after all, what did I have to lose?). I went to see a French herbalist in the East Village, a few blocks away from where I lived. With her long straight black hair, pale skin, very thin frame, and extremely thick accent, she seemed like a witch in the best sense of the word.

She took one look at my eyes and told me that I was so sick that I was barely living: "You are almost dead." She pleaded with me to come clean about my drug addiction so that she could help me. I kept telling her over and over that I'd never taken drugs in my life. It was the truth.

She honestly believed I was on heroin or crack. It was bizarre.

I went home with a bag full of herbs to brew and felt a bit like a kick-ass witch myself. Truly though, I was puzzled and confused. After a lot of head-scratching, I finally figured out why she thought what she did!

I was a drug addict! Just not in the sense that most people would think.

I had severe allergies as a kid, which meant that for my entire childhood (from the age of about five years old), I was on multiple pills every single day. I took steroids, used inhalers for my asthma, and received allergy shots a few times a week. Yes, a week. I even brought the shots with me to college and had the health center administer them.

The bottom line was: I *had* been taking drugs my entire life.

So my drug overload was not from anything illegal, but from the years and years of steroids, allergy shots, and allergy pills I took growing up. These are also drugs, but we think that if it's written on a prescription pad or sold over the counter at CVS, it's somehow 'different.'

It's really not. Drugs are drugs.

They are still toxic substances that mess with your body and mask symptoms. You may feel better for a while, but if the underlying issue isn't addressed, it won't be a lasting fix.

For me, all that toxicity had finally caught up. The herbalist called me "terminally ill." My liver was failing and that was why I was in severe pain.

Knowing this, I went through a massive detox. This was before detoxes were well-known! (I had never heard of one prior). I pursued a natural and holistic approach. I drank pungent herbal teas and even ate clay.

I "went vegan" and juiced long before it was easy or trendy. In a lot of ways, I was paving my own path.

This was before NYC had juice bars on every corner (Liquiteria, a cold press juice bar was the only option!). Veganism was also a hard sell. There was maybe one or two vegan restaurants I knew of, and even explaining my new "diet" to my family was a challenge. The "no eggs" part especially threw them for a loop!

But the effort was worth it. My strategy worked!

FOOD HEALS

I was amazed that given the opportunity, my body was able to heal itself when no amount of medical intervention helped. I knew this was something I wanted to share, but didn't know how to do it.

Fast forward a few years. I had moved to LA to pursue my acting career, but while there my marriage ended. I was still in my 20s and battling the aftermath of a heart-wrenching divorce all on my own. The situation sent me spiraling into depression. Somehow, I was also juggling life as an actress, artist, gemologist, massage therapist, shiatsu practitioner, and realtor.

As a recovering "drug addict," I refused to take pills of any kind — Tylenol included — even though both my doctor and my therapist wanted to put me on antidepressants to help me get through the pain of my divorce. I just said, "No."

Instead, sugar became my savior. I literally couldn't go a day without chocolate. I found solace in the bottom of pints (and pints and pints) of creamy vegan ice cream.

I remember driving to Whole Foods in tears one day and snapping up six pints of the stuff. Even though the cashier gave me a look — okay, I 'might' have also been crying at the time — it was gone in two days.

I'd scarf packets of chocolate chips, Twizzlers, Swedish Fish, candy, sorbet — anything and everything I could get my hands on in a bid to mend my broken heart.

Since I wasn't putting on weight (if anything, I was the thinnest I'd been in my adult life), I thought my binges were perfectly normal and acceptable considering everything I was going through.

It wasn't until after I moved back to New York that it caught up with me. I couldn't move. I was exhausted for weeks and months on end. I felt like I was 80 years old and got sick constantly. I knew that there had to be a better way, and thought back to my experience years earlier.

The first step was admitting I had a problem. The second step was seeking help - in all the right places.

I spent years learning holistic approaches to health. I saw an acupuncturist, massage therapists and integrative doctors. I became a certified Shiatsu practitioner, a licensed massage therapist, and an IntenSati fitness leader, but it wasn't until I learned about the Institute for Integrative Nutrition (IIN) that I finally found out how to use my experiences to help others.

It was like my eureka moment! Health Coaching, *of course!*

At IIN, I studied over 100 dietary theories and many cutting-edge studies about how an integrative and holistic approach to wellness has all sorts of amazing outcomes, like the one I had years ago.

Today, I've hardly had a cold in over six years and my allergies have been at bay for over a decade. My energy is back in full force. I'm happy - really happy. I meditate daily, make self care a priority, eat an organic (as much as possible) plant-based diet, and move my body as often as I can.

I am remarried to an incredible, dedicated, loyal, loving, and devoted husband. We have two beautiful daughters, to whom I gave birth naturally (zero drugs at all!). The younger one was even a home water birth, born in the middle of my kitchen floor. On purpose. It was one of the most empowering experiences of my life and my body did it all on its own.

As a board certified holistic health and wellness coach, I'm thrilled to be able to share my knowledge and experience with others and help guide them to their healthiest and happiest self.

Life is what you make it. And those small steps really do add up. I'm living proof.

It doesn't always have to be so drastic as a complete change in one's diet (although depending on the issues you are facing, that might be the best way forward.)

We are totally capable of healing ourselves through small and easy changes to our lifestyle and food choices. Sometimes the simplest things are the best (for you, the planet, the environment, and your wallet too!).

Eat fresh, organic fruits and vegetables — real food that your grandmother would recognize — cut out toxic drugs, people and situations, and be physically active daily (including spending time outside and in nature). These are all things that are easy to do and have a huge impact on your health.

FOOD HEALS

So as a holistic health coach, let me remind you to look at your whole self. Look at your entire being. Your spirituality, nutrition, fitness, mindset, and relationships all work together. That is what makes up 'you.'

So go out there and live, in the truest sense of the word.

You are 100% capable of healing yourself. You just need to trust your body and give it the right support to do so.

Abby Phon is a Board Certified Holistic Health Coach, public speaker, and vegan YouTube home chef. She leads corporate workshops on nutrition, meditation, stress relief, and essential oils to companies like Google and WeWork.

She's written over 40 articles for MindBodyGreen and is a mom of two young daughters and a rescue rabbit.

Follow her work at AbbyPhon.com.

CHAPTER 5 – JOE CROSS: FROM FAT, SICK & NEARLY DEAD TO THRIVING

From Fat, Sick & Nearly Dead to Thriving

By: Joe Cross

Filed Under:
#foodheals #nutritionheals #juiceheals

I've found that we humans spend the first 40 years of our lives trying to kill ourselves and the next 40 trying to stay alive. That was certainly the case for me.

I started putting on weight around age 20, and by the time I was 40 years old, I was more than a 100 pounds overweight. I was stressed, I smoked cigarettes. I wasn't exercising and I was eating all processed refined foods.

I thought a vegetable was something you put on your hamburger!

Not only was I fat, but I was sick too.

At the age of 32, I woke up one day and my entire body was swollen and itchy. I went straight to the hospital, but they couldn't figure out what was wrong with me, so they just started pumping me full of steroids.

I was later diagnosed with an autoimmune disease called chronic urticaria.

I knew the situation wasn't great, but I thought, "Lucky me, to live in the age of modern medicine! I don't need to change my life, I can just fix it all with a pill!"

When I asked my doctor when I could get off the pills, he told me the bad news: "Never."

In all likelihood, I'd be on medications for the rest of my life.

But I still wasn't ready to take responsibility for my own health. Instead, I decided to visit every doctor I could find. Surely one of them would fix me!

For the next five years, I traveled around the world and spent a ridiculous amount of money consulting with every doctor who was willing to see me.

They took my blood out, they put my blood back in. They put me on a hundred different medications, but nothing seemed to work.

So then I thought I'd try alternative medicine.

If Western medicine wasn't doing the trick, maybe nontraditional therapies held the key. I went to witch doctors, I took mud baths, I consulted with experts in Chinese medicine.

I tried everything I could find, but still nothing seemed to work.

Then, on the eve of my 40th birthday, I looked in the mirror and I was shocked at what I saw looking back at me.

Could this fat, sick man really be me?

And finally, after all those years, I had my *aha!* moment. Maybe I didn't need more doctors or more therapies. Maybe what I really needed all along was just to listen to my own body.

I thought back to something that one of my doctors had told me on my years-long medical walkabout: "You know, Joe, 70% of diseases are caused by lifestyle choices."

I finally allowed myself to really process that truth. 70% of the diseases we suffer from are caused by things we do to ourselves. They are caused by what we eat, what we drink, how we process stress, how much sleep we get (or don't).

I went down that list and I realized that if lifestyle was a report card, I was earning an 'F' in every class.

I was failing my own body through the choices I made each day.

In that moment, I realized how much I'd been prioritizing wealth instead of health. I knew I needed to overhaul my entire values system and focus on healing myself.

I decided to take the same approach to health that I'd taken in business: logic.

FOOD HEALS

Humans are the top species on Earth. How did we get here?

Well, for most of our time on this planet, we weren't eating Big Macs and corn syrup. We got to where we are by eating plants; after all, what are plants but energy harnessed directly from the sun?

So I reasoned that the best approach would be to return to what my ancestors ate. I decided to try eating only plants for two years, and if after that I was still sick, then I'd just have to accept that I was part of that unlucky 30% who couldn't cure themselves by changing their lifestyle.

I still saw a problem though. I needed to consume all of these fruits and vegetables for their energy, but I still needed to lose weight.

So I jump-started my journey with juicing.

For 60 days, I consumed only juice: kale juice, apple juice, pineapple juice, cucumber juice, as many juices as I could manage.

I followed an 80/20 rule (80% vegetables and 20% fruits) to make sure I wasn't consuming too much sugar, and I tried to mix it up as much as possible to make sure I was getting a wide variety of nutrients.

For those first 60 days, I drank six glasses of juice a day.

I won't lie, the first five days were rough. My body was detoxing from everything I'd been pumping into it for 40 years, and the emotional attachment we have to food is huge.

But after I got through those first few days, I felt absolutely fantastic. Not only did I lose 82 pounds in the first 60 days of juicing, I was feeling like a million bucks.

When my 60-day juice cleanse was complete, I switched to my current plant-based diet. I ate only fruits, vegetables, nuts, seeds, and whole grains, harnessing the power of the sun just like my ancestors did.

I continued losing weight, my cholesterol levels dropped, and within months I was fully off my medications.

JOE CROSS

Doctors had been telling me for years that I would need to take these pills for the rest of my life, and here I was, completely pill-free after only five months of a plant-based diet.

I have a lot of respect for doctors and I believe they mean well, but if you only eat food made from people in white coats, you're going to start seeing people in white coats.

It's not that my doctors didn't tell me that I could cure myself with a plant-based diet for some nefarious reason; it's just that they didn't think I would actually do it.

All they had the power to do was to prescribe pills.

The power to make lifestyle changes was all up to me.

I was so inspired by how juicing and a plant-based diet healed my body that I knew I had to share my journey with the world. I created the film *Fat, Sick & Nearly Dead* to show everyone the incredible effect that fruits and vegetables had on my life and to hopefully inspire people to make similar changes in their own lives.

I've since released a sequel, *Fat, Sick & Nearly Dead 2* about maintaining these strategies long-term, published several books, made another film called *The Kids Menu*, and I've started the organization *Reboot With Joe*.

I love talking with people all across the world about the incredible power of plants and now have many programs and products to help people on this journey.

I believe our cells are meant to function well, that they're meant to play in perfect harmony in this beautiful symphony of life. We just have to treat them with respect and to think about our health holistically.

And for me, the number one way to do that is with the fuel that I put in my body.

Food absolutely does heal!

If I can do it, you can do it too.

It's never too late to reboot your health!

As a celebrated health and wellness leader, Joe Cross inspires others to get healthy and lose weight through juicing and eating more plants and vegetables.

Joe transformed from being obese and sick with a crippling autoimmune disease to losing weight and feeling his best during a 60-day juice fast, which he named a "Reboot."

Follow his journey at RebootWithJoe.com.

Food Heals Podcast Episodes 4 & 73

CHAPTER 6 – CHRIS WARK: FOOD HELPED HEAL MY CANCER

Food Helped Heal My Cancer

By: Chris Wark

Filed Under:
#foodheals #thejourneyheals #nutritionheals

I was only 26 years old and it was two days before Christmas when I received the worst news of my life.

I had cancer.

Up until that point, I was a typical American. I was constantly stressed and I ate a lot of junk food, but I figured I looked fine and I felt healthy, so what was the problem?

Except I didn't feel healthy. Not really.

I had this deep abdominal pain that would come and go, but because it wasn't a steady, unrelenting pain I figured it couldn't be that serious. I thought I just had an ulcer.

In 2003, I finally went in for a colonoscopy, where doctors discovered a golf-ball-sized tumor in my colon. They took a biopsy of the tumor and then called me with the bad news.

I had colon cancer.

I was in shock. I was so young, I thought I was healthy, and I'd just gotten married two years prior. How many anniversaries did I have left? How many birthdays? Was this going to be my story?

My whole world was turned upside down.

A week after Christmas, I had surgery to remove the tumor. When I woke up, a doctor was there to deliver even more bad news: "It was worse than we thought, stage 3c."

The cancer had spread to my lymph nodes and my only option (or so the doctors told me) was 9 to 12 months of chemotherapy.

I was overwhelmed and doped up on pain medication, but a few things had already started to make me think, started to make me question what I was being told.

The very first meal they served me after my surgery was a Sloppy Joe. That's right, the staple of summer camp, grade school, and prison lunch lines was also being served to cancer patients.

Red meat is a Group 2 carcinogen! Of course, I didn't know about that back then; I just knew that something felt wrong.

Then I asked the doctor if there were any foods I should avoid — after all, they'd just cut out a section of my guts and sewed me back together. But his response was surprisingly blasé, "Nah, just don't lift anything heavier than a beer."

The truth started sinking in: the medical industry doesn't care about nutrition.

Recovering from the surgery at home, I saw the train of chemotherapy barrelling down the tracks towards me. I was afraid, and not just because I knew it would be tough. The idea of poisoning myself just didn't make sense. I wanted to build my body up, not tear it down more. But I didn't know what to do. I didn't know if there was an alternative.

My wife and I prayed about it. I asked God to please give me a sign if there was another way, a way to fight my cancer without chemo.

Two days later, a book arrived at my doorstep. The book, sent to me by a friend of my dad's, was all about healing cancer through healthy eating. The author had healed his own color cancer using healthy living and nutrition.

I was only a few chapters in when I started to cry.

There, reading this book alone on my couch, it all hit me. Maybe it was my lifestyle that was killing me. And if that was true, maybe I had the tools to heal myself too. "It worked for this guy, and he's just a regular human," I thought. "I'm human, maybe it can work for me."

I immediately called my wife. My thoughts and plans all started bursting forth over the phone: I was going to get a juicer, I was going to switch to a raw food diet, and I wasn't going to do chemotherapy. And my lovely wife, sitting there in her cubicle staring at spreadsheets, did her very best to listen and understand.

Our friends and family members, however, were not so on board.

"Don't you think if there was a better way, the doctors would know about it?" they demanded, terrified for my life. "I know someone who tried alternative therapy for their cancer and they died."

So there I was with this terrible reality and this impossible decision weighing on me, and everyone from the medical industry to my family was telling me that I was crazy.

But I called my mom, and to my wonderful surprise, she was incredibly supportive. She actually had a whole library of books about nutrition and natural healing at home. I decided that, regardless of what I was going to do about chemotherapy, I needed to make massive changes to my diet and lifestyle.

I adopted a 100% raw food diet and started juicing carrots right away.

It all made sense to me. God created fruits and vegetables for us to sustain us and keep us healthy. Our bodies don't need anything that comes in a package or anything that's made in a factory; the Earth already has everything that we need.

But my other family members pressured me into seeing a doctor again. The appointment didn't go so great. The oncologist told me I had a 60% chance of making it five years— not a 60% chance of being cured, mind you, just of being alive.

I asked him about alternative therapies and he shut me down immediately. "If you don't do chemotherapy," he told me, "you're insane."

Not only that, but he also told me that I couldn't eat a raw food diet because it would fight the chemo. But apparently, Sloppy Joes and beers were fine for cancer patients. It didn't add up.

The oncologist used fear to manipulate me, and on my way out, I did what a cancer patient is supposed to do: I made an appointment to start chemotherapy in a few weeks.

CHRIS WARK

I was hopeless, discouraged, and afraid, but I went home and fired up my juicer and stuck with my holistic healing plan.

Three weeks later, when the time came for my chemo port installation I knew that I had to say no. I wasn't ready to do chemotherapy, so I opted out.

I didn't know what the future had in store for me, but I knew I wanted to focus on building up my body, not tearing it down further.

I made a decision to live or die on my own terms and I knew that chemotherapy was always an option down the road if I couldn't restore my health.

I slowly put together a support system: my wife, my mom, a naturopath, and an integrative oncologist. I realized that cancer isn't the cause of a sick body, it's the effect of a sick body.

Rather than poisoning my body with the toxic chemotherapy, I overdosed on nutrition instead. I ate only raw natural foods and I drank so much carrot juice I turned orange!

And part of living or dying on my terms meant thinking about the future. I realized how much I wanted to be a dad. It was a big decision; after all, we didn't know how long I'd be around. But my brave, amazing wife said "yes," not knowing how long I would be around to help her raise our child.

Thirteen months later, I was back in the hospital. But this time, I wasn't there because of cancer. This time, I was there to welcome our beautiful baby girl into the world.

Today, my daughter is 14 years old, her younger sister is 10, and I'm healthy, strong, and cancer free! I'm not on a 100% raw diet anymore, but I still eat an organic, whole foods, plant-based diet to maintain my health.

I've come to view the terminology we use around cancer — battling cancer, fighting cancer — to be the wrong way of looking at it.

It's not about fighting your body, it's about giving it the support it needs to heal itself.

Regardless of which therapies you choose, the best way to support your body's ability to heal is with the natural foods that the Earth provides for us: fruits and vegetables, nuts, seeds, legumes, whole grains, and fresh juices.

Restoring your health and reversing chronic disease often requires massive action and radical diet and lifestyle changes, which aren't easy.

But when you realize that your choices today create your life tomorrow and that your choices can mean the difference between life and death, it's worth it!

Chris Wark is a global wellness leader and author of the national bestselling book *Chris Beat Cancer: A Comprehensive Plan for Healing Naturally*. He has made many appearances on radio, television, and documentaries, including the award-winning documentary film *The C Word*.

Chris inspires countless people to take control of their health and reverse disease with a radical transformation of diet and lifestyle. He reaches millions of people per year through his website and social media channels.

Connect with Chris at ChrisBeatCancer.com.

***Food Heals Podcast* Episode 236**

CHAPTER 7 – WHITNEY LAURITSEN: HEALING "NOT GOOD ENOUGH"

Healing "Not Good Enough"

By: Whitney Lauritsen

Filed Under:
#foodheals #spiritheals #loveheals

I was about 10 years old when I started believing that my body wasn't good enough. Around that time, I had an interest in acting and dreamed of being in TV shows and movies.

As part of my quest to achieve this, a friend of my parents with on-camera experience gave me some tips. During our conversation, she took out a measuring tape and placed it around my waist, concluding that I might not be trim enough for casting agents.

She showed me some exercises, and then I took it upon myself to find more ways to slim down.

Not long after that, a friend my age shared how she lost weight: she didn't eat for a day. How easy!

That was the beginning of a lifelong obsession with getting my body to be the "right size."

Along with associating success with physical measurements, I concluded that boys would never like me because I was teased for having big lips and looking chubby in my bathing suit.

All before the age of 13.

The heartbreaking part? I'm not alone. It seems like a rite of passage for girls to experience external criticism for their bodies.

What some may think of as a harmless comment can spark a long battle with body dysmorphia, eating disorders, and low self-esteem.

WHITNEY LAURITSEN

Many of us spend most of our lives feeling not good enough and trying to mold ourselves into what we think looks acceptable and desirable.

Between the ages of 13 and 18, I tried every trick in the book. Low fat meals, diet shakes, sugar-free soda, appetite suppression pills, fitness plans from magazines, workout videos...and purging. I'm not sure what triggered the beginning of the latter because it's now a distant memory.

But I vividly recall how it came to an end.

When I first started, purging meals felt like a great solution to counterbalance my love for food. To this day I love food so much and deeply enjoy trying new flavors and textures.

Like a typical teenager, I felt joy snacking after school with my friends. Yet, as my insecurities about my body evolved, I felt a lot of shame about what and how I ate. I felt confused about calories, fat, sugar, oil, and salt.

I didn't understand what moderation meant.

Working out didn't give me the results I wanted, and all the weight loss tricks I tried didn't seem to help much either. So, I decided that purging was the best option. It became my go-to whenever I felt like I ate too much and feared it would add on more pounds.

Things changed my freshman year of college.

Something inside me realized that I had a problem and I should get help. Somehow I found the courage to bring it up to a nurse during a physical, and she recommended I see a specialist.

First, I went to see a nutritionist, which felt like a waste of time because everything she mentioned about food seemed very logical. Doesn't everyone know that fruit and vegetables are healthy choices?

Knowledge wasn't going to fix my disordered relationship with my body. I needed emotional support, so that was recommended next.

A few sessions with a therapist were truly life-changing. She was the first to ask me why I was purging. Not a surface level why. A deep down inside why.

FOOD HEALS

She helped me explore my emotions, experiences, and relationships like never before. I had some "ah ha" moments that impacted my life from then on. It was like a switch was flipped and everything clicked.

I haven't purged since.

My self-esteem about my body is still a work in progress. Even though I no longer purge, every day I hear a little voice inside my head telling me that I'm not doing enough to make my body look right. I frequently examine my body in the mirror; even on the days I feel good about it I always find something that "needs work."

Fortunately, the voice is quieter than it was in my teens, and I have developed more tools to shift out of negative thinking.

I'm not sure it will ever be silent, but I hope it becomes a faint whisper one day.

It was during the same year of my first therapy sessions that I was introduced to veganism. I attended a liberal college that served vegan ice cream and other plant-based options in the cafeteria.

The next year I met a cool student who was vegan and our conversations about it sparked my curiosity.

The year after that, a guy I had a crush on went vegan and I figured I might impress him if I tried the diet myself. Little did I know that eating a plant-based diet would have another enormous, positive impact on my relationship with food and my body.

At first, I dabbled in the vegetarian diet. Within months my body completely transformed.

Pounds slipped off simply by avoiding meat and dairy. People often asked me what my secret was, and their positive attention gave me a sense of physical confidence I don't recall feeling prior to that.

Six months into being vegetarian, I upgraded to the vegan diet, and I felt so in alignment with the lifestyle that I never turned back. My body felt and looked better than ever (in my opinion), and most importantly, I felt like I could eat freely without the urge to purge or criticize my food choices.

Veganism felt magical. For the first few years I thought I could eat anything and not gain a pound or ever get sick.

While that's the case for some people, unfortunately it's not always like that for me. The weight I lost started to come back on. My arms, face, and stomach began to look inflamed and I developed very unpleasant allergy-like symptoms that doctors couldn't diagnose.

Once again, I felt in a battle with my body. But this time, I was determined to find a healthy way to change it.

I went on a hunt to get to the root of my allergies (or whatever was causing my body to frequently sneeze, flare up, and drain my energy).

I tried every natural remedy I could find at the markets plus Eastern health modalities like acupuncture. When I ran out of ideas, I even resorted to medical prescriptions like nasal sprays because I couldn't stand how awful I felt most days of the week.

I finally discovered the magic of nasal washing with a neti pot, which relieved most of my sinus challenges.

But ultimately, there was still something off...until a friend visited me.

For my birthday one year, my best friend flew to Los Angeles to celebrate. When she arrived, she explained that she was experimenting with a gluten-free diet, something that was slowly becoming a new health trend.

It felt easier to exclude gluten from both our plates while she was in town, so I joined her in creative conquests to avoid wheat and other glutinous products. It was fun and pretty easy! So much so that I kept going even after she left.

And within weeks, I started to feel better.

Similar to how trying the plant-based diet helped me feel more positive about my food choices, going gluten-free helped me discover that I was sensitive to certain foods. My trial run encouraged me to experiment with removing or reducing other ingredients from my meals.

Much to my surprise, I discovered that I have reactions to soy, corn, and almonds.

Taking those items out of my diet put an end to symptoms I had struggled with my entire life, including chronic sneezing, scalp itchiness, digestive challenges, and inflammation. In addition to shedding uncomfortable health challenges, I shed much of the weight and bloating I had struggled with most of my life.

No more battles. Nutrition, fitness, and overall wellness have become passions of mine. I enjoy finding ways to feel my best and appreciate my body for how it looks in the present moment.

While in the past I found health confusing and overwhelming, I now find it fascinating and empowering.

I find joy in learning new ways to care for my body and how to embrace whatever flaws I used to perceive, so much so that I built a career around teaching others about wellness so they too can heal.

I give credit to wellness — mentally and physically — for helping me heal inside and out.

Learning how to navigate my emotions and reactions through therapy and spirituality was deeply impactful. And equal credit goes to my dietary changes, which taught me how to be in touch with my body like never before.

It's incredibly empowering to feel love, appreciation, and friendship with my body.

While I may never be fully free of the critical self-talk, I'm grateful that I'm no longer under its spell.

And doesn't everyone wish to break free of those mental chains?

Since 2008, Whitney Lauritsen has been creating video content, digital products, and online training about healthy living and wellness entrepreneurship.

She is the founder of several brands (Eco-Vegan Gal, Wellevatr, and Creative Wellth) and is author of *Healthy, Organic Vegan on a Budget*.

Receive personal and professional guidance at WhitneyLauritsen.com.

Food Heals Podcast Episodes 5, 11, 21, 112, 113, 165, 172, 173, 174, 175, 176, 203, 208, 215, 221, 228, 237, 240, 250, 251, 254 & 264

CHAPTER 8 – ADAM SCHAEUBLE: THE POWER OF PUTTING ACTION BEHIND THE LAW OF ATTRACTION

The Power of Putting ACTION Behind the Law of Attraction

By: Adam Schaeuble

Filed Under:
#foodheals #theuniverseheals #thejourneyheals

On July 12, 2007 I hit rock bottom.

I weighed 327 pounds, I had $40,000 in credit card debt, my career was at a dead end, and the woman I fell in love with was moving away. I had become a full on "crap-magnet" and my close friends had taken notice.

They started "letting me borrow" personal growth materials like books from Tony Robbins and there was this DVD called *The Secret* that two different friends sent my direction.

I remember getting home that evening and seeing the DVD that had been sitting on top of my DVD player for a couple of weeks collecting dust. For the first time, I felt like I was supposed to actually watch it.

This was the first time I had ever been exposed to any sort of personal growth material in my life, and it set my soul on fire. For the first time in my life, I felt like I was the one who got to call the shots.

In that moment, I was able to reclaim control over the direction of my life and it all started with the Law of Attraction.

That night I sat down and decided what my life was going to look like in exactly five years from the current date. I wrote out every life goal that I would achieve. But I also knew that this wouldn't be enough.

I had set goals before and they ended up being lost in the shuffle of my busy life.

I knew I had to have daily accountability to show up for my new life that I was determined to create for myself.

You can't spell "ATTRACTION" without "ACTION," so I created what I refer to now as my Lifestyle Rehabilitation Statement.

The rules of my Lifestyle Rehabilitation Statement were as follows:

1. It had to be written in present tense. I was not allowed to say things like, "I want to lose 100lbs." Instead, I said, "I've lost 100lbs."

2. It had to be super positive and full of energy. I was not allowed to say things like, "I want to be free from debt!" I didn't want to focus on a negative word like "debt," so instead I wrote, "I live my life with total satisfaction and abundance!"

3. It had to fire me up! If I started to not be excited about reaching one of the goals, I was allowed to change it.

4. There had to be a strong 'why' behind each goal statement like, "I've lost 100lbs and I feel amazing. I'm energized, confident, and comfortable in my own skin, and you can't get me to stop smiling! I lead by example for the people I love the most."

5. I had to read the statement out loud every single day — morning and night — until I achieved every goal or the five year deadline passed.

Now if I've acquired one super human power in my life it is that I am able to implement and take action consistently.

Remember, the law of attraction doesn't work without action.

So, on I went. Every morning, I read my statement out loud as soon as I woke up. I read it with passion and energy and really tried to put myself into each goal I was striving for.

I tried to feel what I would feel like in that moment when the goal was achieved.

This set the tone for my day and focused me. I had my eyes open for opportunities to make progress toward one of my goals. Maybe I would meet someone who could help me with a new business idea or maybe I would find a book that would help me figure out my debt situation.

Before I started this process, I felt as though I were standing in a long, dark tunnel.

There were doors of opportunity opening and closing but I just couldn't see them. By using my Lifestyle Rehabilitation Statement process, I was able to flip on the light switch and see the opportunities that were there right in front of me, and I could choose to take action.

Every evening, I would end the day with another round with my statement. This was my accountability time. I knew that I absolutely had to move the needle in the right direction in at least one of my goal areas every single day.

Even if I just pushed over the tiniest domino, it was still progress.

So I would read my statement with purpose, passion, and positive energy and then I would ask myself, "Adam, did you show up for these goals today?"

If the answer was "no," then I had to do something before I went to bed — no exceptions — because I realized that I was worth the effort.

So maybe I would knock out a quick workout or read a business book for 20 minutes, but I always did something daily.

I think that was a big deal because so many people get intimidated by their goals.

It's like staring up at a giant mountain and saying, "Damn, that shit is WAY up there!" And then the big scary question is asked, "What if I fail?" And we stop taking action, usually before we even get started.

So instead of staring up at the peak of the mountain, I chose to focus on the next step right in front of me and winning the next moment of decision.

FOOD HEALS

The cool thing is that my momentum started to build.

I found a couple of amazing books about reducing debt and I put a plan of action into place. I immediately felt like I had stopped digging myself into a financial hole and I was now in control.

I made it a daily ritual to treat my body with the respect it deserves with things like proper nutrition, exercise, and brain food (reading books and blogs!).

I started to drop a lot of body fat and others started to ask me to help them out.

I joined a martial arts program and started making connections right away. I even worked up the courage to ask the owners if I could rent floor space a few times a week to help my friends via a bootcamp class, and they said, "Yes!"

And then there was that amazing woman that I was in love with who was moving away. Well, in a strange turn of events, her mortgage fell through and she ended up staying in town and needed a place to stay.

(Spoiler Alert: It's now 12 years later as I write this, and we are still married).

On July 19, 2012, I had achieved the dream life that I had mapped out five years (and seven days!) earlier.

I walked into my brand new 8,000 square-foot fitness studio at 6 AM and there were over a hundred people there ready to learn how to get healthy.

I had lost over 100 pounds and became a leader in my community.

I had helped my hometown clients lose over 35,000 pounds and counting.

I had zero debt and I was well on my way to being mortgage-free as well.

I was married to the woman of my dreams and our first child, Henry, was the most special thing that had happened to me so far.

On that morning, my dream life became my reality because five years prior I decided to put my foot down and realize that I had to be the hero of my own movie.

I believe that the thing that got me from being a goal setter to being a goal achiever was that I was willing to show up for my goals and my dream life every damned day because I am worth it.

And so are you, my friend.

Adam Schaeuble (a.k.a. "The PHD" — previously heavy dude) is the host of *The Million Pound Mission Podcast*. Adam personally lost over 100 pounds and then he helped his hometown lose over 35,000 pounds. Now he's on a mission to produce one million pounds of results around the world.

Follow his journey at MillionPoundMission.com.

Food Heals Podcast **Episodes 235, 237 & 262**

CHAPTER 9 – JOHN SALLEY: HOW TO THRIVE AS AN ATHLETE AND BE A SUPER-SEXY VEGAN

How to Thrive as an Athlete and Be a Super-Sexy Vegan

By: John Salley

Filed Under:
#foodheals #theuniverseheals #thejourneyheals

"This is what you need to do if you want to live," the doctor said.

"What?"

"A colonic," she said.

I didn't know what a colonic was. And, as soon as she explained it, I didn't like the idea. But I needed to get out of chronic pain and I had run out of options.

But let me back up.

Growing up, I was a skinny and sickly kid (not exactly what you'd expect of a future NBA basketball player). The fact was that I didn't eat properly even though I didn't realize it at the time. My mom had two jobs. My dad had two jobs. They did anything they could to feed their growing kid, now a teenager with a compacted colon that no one could diagnose.

I had terrible back pain too and the doctors didn't know what to do. After trying a few different things, I found acupuncture, and it was the first thing that really helped, opening my eyes to alternative forms of medicine.

Next, I met a doctor who helped my father — they thought he had diabetes, but it turned out it was cancer. With treatment, my father made it through that first time, and I wanted to make it through and get better too.

When I was 18, my back pain was still flaring up. A friend at Brooklyn College asked what I ate. I told him how my mother fed me hamburger patties. I would put a patty on the stove, go for my

FOOD HEALS

morning run, come back (that's how fast I was running in high school), flip the patty, get in the shower, flip it again, get out of the shower, and cook my eggs. That was breakfast.

Lunch was a turkey hero sandwich with a thin slice of tomato and a little bit of lettuce. After basketball practice, I'd eat a bagel and drink a fruit juice that didn't actually have real fruit in it.

At dinner, I ate whatever my mom cooked. I was constantly eating things that were made in factories. I had no idea that the stuff I was putting in my body wasn't nourishing me, but was actually slowly destroying each organ.

As a flesh eater, meat had to go through my slow digestive tract. Humans don't have the acids that cats and dogs have to break down meat; our stomach acids are too weak.

If I eat a flesh-based diet, my body cannot handle it. Instead, so much mucus builds up that the immune system is constantly fighting the bad bacteria that the meat adds to the gut.

And eggs? Pure cholesterol.

Meat and eggs —with all their bad bacteria and cholesterol — wreak havoc on our hearts, guts, and other organs. It's really that simple.

When I found out that I had a compacted colon during my senior year in high school, it didn't get any better and continued into college. I tried acupuncture, a chiropractor, and massage, but the problems kept happening and the back pain kept coming back.

That's when I met the amazing new doctor who suggested the colonic. I had to get rid of any preconceived notions I had about the procedure. It helped that this doctor was astounding: She was in her 80s and walked around like a 50-year-old. I was impressed.

And I wanted to get better naturally, so I went for it.

I lost 12 pounds after the first colonic.

I lost more and more weight after each colonic. It was amazing.

I immediately went on a macrobiotic diet and felt better instantly. My body didn't have to fight what was going on in my intestines anymore. I played ball better. My body didn't have to fight itself anymore.

Everything was in harmony for a while.

In 1991, in the middle of my NBA career, I became a "lying vegetarian" — I gave up meat but still ate fish and was in terrible health. I had adult acne. I had the cholesterol of a 37-year-old man at age 27. I was playing hard and had made a name for myself in the league, but they wanted to talk about putting me on pills.

The doctors said my problems were genetic (doctors always want to blame heredity), but I didn't believe it.

I wanted to know *how* it happened.

As an athlete, I was led to believe that egg whites were going to make me stronger and help me keep going. My poor health affected my performance. I was going back and forth with my diet. I would still eat turkey on Thanksgiving. Occasionally, I ate fish, especially salmon (which is actually the most toxic because of pollution or unsafe farming).

Although my diet was better than when I was a kid, every time my back problems returned, I got a colonic. It worked temporarily, but I had to keep going back.

It made me realize that I had to really look at what I was eating on a regular basis and make sustainable choices.

It was time to seriously change my diet.

First, I looked to martial artists who were in great shape, aging incredibly well, and built like me. They had the stamina, agility, performance, and health I was looking for. What did they all have in common?

They were *vegan.*

For athletes on a vegan diet, recovery time is shorter. The diet helps build your lungs. Every organ you are using is working in your benefit.

Our bodies are like a Nascar race car. Get to the root of the problems under the hood, and you figure out the mechanics of everything needed in order to fix things. If you understand the inner workings, you can squash a situation before it becomes a problem.

This is how to handle our health too.

What we eat goes into our bodies on a cellular level.

Today, we have all these strong Africans living in America, but in their middle age, their health declines. I watched it with my parents on insulin. I watched it with my father's cancer.

I didn't understand why everyone in my family was weak and dying of cancer. And then I realized we were all eating the same recipes. All the things inside our home were killing us. If our food costs a dollar at the drive-thru, that's a problem. Food *should* cost more than a dollar.

Expensive food is cheaper than doctors' bills. It's all trade offs.

What is really important to us?

We talk about beauty being on the inside but don't think about what is actually happening on the inside. The stomach, liver, kidneys, and intestines all need to be healthy and functioning well. They need to be nourished, cleansed, and hydrated. What's happening on the inside is reflected on the outside.

My message today is: eat a plant-based diet.

A plant-based diet will change your life and keep you out of the hospital.

I was very religious growing up, and in reading the scriptures, I was taught: "Blessed are the meek: for they shall inherit the earth."

Great men and women — Mother Theresa, Martin Luther King, Che Guevara — are humble because they don't want to be a part of the problem but part of the solution. That's my spirituality piece and perspective.

I try to be the best person I can possibly be, so that I can give the best person I can to the rest of the world.

I have played for three championship teams, but this is my work now.

When I went to India to meet the Dalai Lama, I landed in New Deli and realized the problems I thought I had were not problems at all. I thought I grew up in the hood, but realized I grew up in luxury.

I am a mere speck in this vast universe. But if I die, the universe dies, because I am the universe.

That is who I am. Former champion. Vegan. Advocate. Continuous learner.

I'm not saying I'm totally enlightened, but my eyes are open to the lies we've been told. And I want to enlighten others.

Without change, nothing changes. With change, everything changes.

John Salley is a father, athlete, actor, entrepreneur, talk show host, philanthropist, wellness advocate, vegan, and champion. A proud native of Brooklyn, New York, John was the first NBA player to win four championships with three different teams (Detroit Pistons in 1989 & 1990, Chicago Bulls in 1996, and L.A. Lakers in 2000).

John has adopted a plant-based (raw vegan) lifestyle and is a frequent speaker at VegFests across the USA.

As a Wellness Advocate, one of John's main missions in life is to continue to educate people on the benefits of living a healthier lifestyle through better eating habits.

Food Heals Podcast **Episodes 13, 16, 54 & 55**

CHAPTER 10 – JACQUI LETRAN: MY DEAREST ONE

My Dearest One

By: Jacqui Letran

Filed Under:
#loveheals #thejourneyheals #braveryheals

My Dearest One,

Today is the worst day of my life.

I just found out I am pregnant, and now I have to make the hardest decision I have ever had to make. Words cannot express how sorry I am. I don't know how to take care of you.

You see, I'm only a child myself. At 16, I can barely take care of myself; how can I take care of you? I have nothing to give you. I am just a good-for-nothing troublemaker. All I do is cause pain and destruction wherever I go.

So, my Dearest One, even though it's breaking my heart, I have to do the unthinkable. This is the only choice I have.

To bring you into this world would mean I would doom you to a life of misery, pain, and poverty. I can't do that. I won't do that.

You don't deserve this so-called "existence" that I have to offer you...

I remember writing this letter to my unborn child as if it were yesterday. Earlier that morning, I had gone to a health clinic to get on birth control. I had recently become sexually active and knew that I did not want to get pregnant.

FOOD HEALS

It was my third attempt to get birth control. During the first two visits to the clinic, I felt so terrified, so judged, and so unwelcomed that before my name was called, I silently walked out. This time, I told myself, I would stay and submit to the dreaded pap smear because the alternative of getting pregnant would be far worse.

I remember lying on the exam table, with my feet up on the stirrups, naked from the waist down, with only a thin paper drape covering my lap. I was so scared that I was shaking. I did all I could to distract myself from what was about to happen, but no matter how hard I tried, I couldn't stop the fear.

I thought I was afraid then, but nothing compared to the next few minutes.

A male physician came into my room and picked up my chart without so much as a glance my way or even the courtesy of a greeting. He flipped through my chart, walked toward me, smacked my backside with the chart and said, "Get dressed. You don't need birth control. You're pregnant."

My whole world froze. Everything moved in slow motion. I couldn't move. I couldn't speak.

The doctor was telling me something, but I couldn't hear a word he was saying.

"You're pregnant!" kept reverberating inside my head. I tried so hard to hold back the tears that poured out uncontrollably. I'm sure it lasted only a few minutes, but it felt like an eternity.

Somehow I managed to make my way home. I don't remember much more about that day except for lying in my bed sobbing quietly so my mother couldn't hear me. And I wrote that letter.

I knew I had nothing to give. I knew I was incapable of being a mother. I had to do the one thing I told myself I would never do – have an abortion.

It had been years since I had written in a journal. I used to love writing in my diary until one day I caught my mother reading my most private thoughts without my permission. Since then I decided never to write down such personal things ever again. I did not want to be exposed and vulnerable. I did not want anyone to know my deepest fears, doubts, or shame.

But that night was different.

That night, I felt compelled to write. I was making a decision to end the life of my unborn child before it even had a chance to breathe fresh air. The only way I knew how to honor this child was by writing an apology letter in advance to explain why I had no choice. I hoped that somehow, this act of expressing my sincere remorse would earn me forgiveness.

I continued to sob as the words flowed freely from my heart. Everything became blurry as my eyelids swelled up around a stream of tears that wouldn't stop.

I felt every ounce of life drained out of me, yet, I kept writing.

My Dearest One,

You deserve so much – so much more than I have to offer you. You deserve everything good in life...a mom who can take care of you, love you, and show you every day that you are the most magnificent thing in life.

How did you get so unlucky to be doomed with me. I have nothing to give. I would only ruin your life.

But who says that? Who says I have nothing to give? Even though I have no clue what I'm doing and I have no clue how I'm going to make it through the pregnancy, let alone the childbirth, and being your mother, I know I have something to give you.

I can give you love. I don't have much, but I could give you that.

My Dearest One,

You don't know me, and I don't know you, yet I feel the warmth of your presence, and it comforts me.

Even though you haven't spoken, I heard you clearly. And it was your voice that helped me to find mine.

FOOD HEALS

The flow of tears stopped. I stood up, and for the first time that day, I could breathe freely.

My Dearest One,

I now know I have choices. I choose you.

What started out as an apology letter to my unborn child took on an unexpected life of its own, and it gave me a new life. At that moment, I found the clarity that poured forth from my own intuition. I knew exactly what to choose for myself and for my unborn child.

I was given a chance. I received a miracle.

I now saw this as an opportunity to decide for myself who I truly am and to realize just how strong I could become.

My pregnancy was every bit as tough and trying as I had imagined, and not because I was in pain or suffering from severe morning sickness. It was brutal for me because of the constant battle with doubt and shame.

I remember doing my best to hide my ever-growing belly. I remember the looks of disgust and judgment from passersby. Many days, I questioned my decision and my ability to parent.

I can still recall the cruel words and condescending remarks from my medical providers – the very people who were supposed to guide me through this scary, unknown territory.

During labor, the nurse had to catheterize me. I squirmed and grimaced out of fear and pain.

She looked sternly at me and said, "A hole is a hole when I can't see it. You either lay still, or I'm going to shove this where I can."

Later, during the peak of a labor contraction, I screamed out in pain. A different nurse shouted at me, "You got yourself into this and you're about to have a baby! So stop acting like one!"

You can't imagine the level of fear, shame, and total disbelief I experienced that day, on top of the physical pain of childbirth. It was worse than any experience of humiliation and inhumane disregard that I could have ever imagined.

Then I heard it – his soft, little cry.

It sounded like the voice of an angel singing to me, reassuring me that everything was going to be okay, that I was okay.

The moment I held my son, my entire world changed in an instant. When I looked into his eyes and held his little fingers, I felt the most powerful, overwhelming feeling of love sweep over me, covering every inch of me with so much joy that my heart felt like it was going to burst.

When our eyes met, I felt healed from the inside out.

I had never experienced a love like that, nor did I know a love like that was even possible.

I now knew why I was put on this earth.

I knew I had to do everything I could to become a person deserving of this little angel's love, my Dearest One's love. I knew it was up to me to break this cycle of poverty, low self-esteem, and extreme self-hatred so I could give this newborn little angel everything he deserved.

I also felt a deep desire to make sure that other teen girls wouldn't have to suffer the pain and humiliation that I had experienced — I could be a source of strength, support, and guidance for them.

When my son, Alan, was four months old, I passed my G.E.D. exam and enrolled in college. Even though I dropped out of 10th grade a year earlier, I was now determined to succeed.

I was a young woman on two very important missions.

Mission #1: Be the person who was deserving of this little boy's love.

Mission #2: Be the person who would champion for other teen girls, to give them a safe place to go so they can learn to make healthy, positive choices for themselves in a supportive and nurturing environment.

FOOD HEALS

My journey into self-love and academic success was long and challenging. I didn't have much self-worth and I didn't have a strong academic foundation. It felt like everything was twice as difficult for me.

So many times I wanted to give up, but in those moments all I had to do was look into my son's eyes or hear his joyous laughter. Each time my son hugged me or called me "Mommy," he recharged me and strengthened my resolve to become "that person" I knew I could be.

I began to devour every self-help book I could get my hands on. I was hungry for knowledge. I was hungry for change.

Through a long and often painful journey into self-love, I learned that all the judgments I felt from others were actually judgments that I held against myself.

Each time I felt judged or looked down upon, it was the voice of my Inner Critic pointing out my flaws and insecurities.

Each time I experienced the pain of feeling unloved or being unlovable, it was the voice of my Inner Critic telling me false stories about myself.

My Inner Critic had mastered the art of projecting fears and self-doubt outward, so I had someone else to blame for all of my mistakes and failures.

For so many years of my life, I allowed my Inner Critic to rob me of self-confidence, self-esteem, and self-worth because I did not understand how my mind worked. I did not know that I could transform my negative internal voice into a voice of love and support.

Once I discovered that my Inner Critic was really just trying to protect me from getting hurt — albeit, in a very misguided way — I took control and became the boss of my life.

I discovered that I had the power to change everything I didn't like about my life.

I discovered that I could give myself a chance to succeed in life and be happy.

I learned that no matter what was happening outside of me, I had the power to choose how I saw the situation. I had the power to choose how to respond and react. I had the power to let go of things that held me back, and to focus on things that brought me happiness and joy.

And best of all, I knew that I had my very own best friend with me 24/7 to guide and support me. And if the inner voice of my new best friend wasn't up for the job at the moment, I had my son who was my number one reason for pursuing evolution with so much passion and determination.

At age 23, I graduated Cum Laude from East Tennessee State University with a Masters Degree in Nursing. I had realized my academic dream of becoming a Nurse Practitioner and was well on my way to creating that safe space for teens to learn about themselves and make good life choices.

I remember the exhilaration of walking across the stage to receive my diploma. Then my six-year-old son ran up to me, gave me a huge hug, and said, "I'm so proud of you, Mommy."

At that moment, my whole world moved in slow motion once again. But this time, it was because I was standing in my power, choosing to savor every single second.

I had come full circle.

That scared, hopeless little girl who felt so unlovable and unworthy was now a strong, loving, independent woman who has so much to give back to the world.

Today, I am on a mission to help teens and young adults discover how damaging their negative internal voice can be. I call it the voice of the Inner Bully.

Today, I help people live a fulfilled life with a deep love for themselves, the planet, and all beings by eating a plant-based diet and hosting the podcast *Roving Vegans*. Because love heals and food heals too.

Today, I share all the tools and techniques that I have learned during my own transformational journey to help others transform their Inner Bully into their Best Friend and Personal Champion for success.

My Dearest One,

I love you more than life itself. Every day my heart is filled with love and gratitude that you chose me to be your mother. You taught me how to love myself unconditionally. You taught me how to give and receive love freely. You opened my heart to endless possibilities and wonderments.

Because of you, I have learned to trust my intuition, to step into my full power, and to live my life with passion and purpose.

My Dearest One, thank you for being my greatest teacher and the greatest love of my life. I am eternally grateful for the miracle of you.

Jacqui Letran is a multi-award-winning author, speaker, mindset mentor, and host of the podcasts *Roving Vegans* and *Stop the Bully Within*. Jacqui teaches that personal power, success, and happiness are achievable by all, regardless of current struggles and circumstances.

Connect with Jacqui at RovingVegans.com.

CHAPTER 11 – SOPHIE ULIANO: LIVING GORGEOUSLY GREEN

Living Gorgeously Green

By: Sophie Uliano

Filed Under:
#foodheals #thejourneyheals #nutritionheals

Living "gorgeously green" is about being happy, being healthy, and taking care of our amazing planet. When we connect with our deepest values, we truly live our most gorgeous life.

It may be hard to believe, but I used to have a real victim mentality. I loved to complain about how hard everything was for me and saw the glass as half empty. I believed that things happened *to* me and not *for* me.

But, in my 20s, I was lucky enough to have a mentor who helped snap me out of it. She taught me that the only way to make a meaningful change in my life was to take full responsibility for it.

If there was something in my life that I didn't like, it was up to me to change it.

And grabbing ahold of that responsibility was the best thing that ever happened to me. I realized that we each have the power to determine the course of our life.

That empowerment is the foundation of everything I do, but my journey with Gorgeously Green didn't really start until a few years later. I was raising my young daughter in Los Angeles, an environment that was vastly different from the idyllic English countryside I grew up in.

And something just didn't feel right.

I saw smog everywhere I went, I worried about my daughter playing in the park because I didn't know what chemicals were sprayed on the grass, and I could even see signs of premature aging in my own skin.

73

So I started to research.

I read hundreds of books and articles, learning more and more about our health and the environment. Then, I wanted to share what I learned with the world. So, I wrote my first book, *Gorgeously Green*, and launched what has turned out to be an absolutely incredible online community. So many others were seeking answers to similar questions I had!

I started my company in 2007, the same year that YouTube was created and before Instagram was even a thing! It was a great time to be an early mover with these amazing platforms.

Now I have tens of thousands of followers over seven digital platforms (a blog, a newsletter, Facebook, Twitter, Instagram, Pinterest, and YouTube) and I make a point to generate new content daily. I also run a healthy weightloss coaching program so that I can work with women on a deeply personal level to achieve their goals.

I've been on *Oprah* and met incredible women like Julia Roberts, I've published multiple bestselling books, and I'm here to tell you... gorgeousness is so much more than skin-deep.

So what does living gorgeously green mean to me?

For starters, I believe that gorgeousness isn't only an external thing. In my teen years and early 20s, I tried so hard to perfect my appearance: every hair in place, every fingernail polished. But deep down, I felt horribly inadequate.

I was burned out, afraid, and disconnected from the world around me. It was only later that I realized that gorgeousness is a quality of energy. It's about living in balance with our bodies and the world around us.

Our bodies are miraculous, and when we nourish ourselves with the foods that nature provides for us, we have a chance to heal ourselves, to maintain optimal health and ideal weight, and to truly stay gorgeous for good.

The most important decision I made was to switch to a plant-based diet. I was raised a meat-eater, but I couldn't ignore the scientific evidence: meat contains cholesterol and saturated fat.

FOOD HEALS

The Presidential Advisory for the American Heart Association has now made it plain and clear that to reduce our risk of disease, we need to minimize dietary saturated fat.

A plant-powered diet is better for our bodies and better for the planet.

And don't worry so much about protein! Americans actually get way too much protein on average and it can be found in all foods, not just meat and dairy. A cup of lentils alone contains over half of our daily recommended protein.

A plant-based diet doesn't have to be boring either. Once we slow down to appreciate the incredible colors, textures, and tastes of the whole foods that come straight from nature, our palettes come alive.

I make it a priority to get to my local farmers' market every Sunday morning. If my green beans or bell peppers have been trucked in from another state -- or, even worse, flown in from another country -- I'm not going to get the full nutrient profile that nature intended for me.

Beautiful fruits and veggies that are as fresh as possible are the mainstay of a really healthy diet.

I'm also passionate about natural organic beauty products. When I started Gorgeously Green, there were fewer than 50 brands on the market that met my standard of "healthy."

Today, there are thousands!

It's amazing that natural beauty is a huge trend right now and I love that the space is changing. But it's still difficult to find skincare and makeup products that are good for our skin, good for the environment, and still deliver outstanding results.

I'm constantly researching products to help my community make the best choices they can. Plus, reviewing beauty products is just a lot of fun!

It hasn't always been easy to balance being a mom and a CEO while at the same time living according to my own healthy philosophy. The biggest challenge for me is always staying on top of current research and trends so I can help the Gorgeously Green community navigate this crazy landscape of wellness and beauty.

There's so much information out there, and it's often confusing and conflicting, so I take my role very seriously. I spend so much time researching and reviewing products that I wish there were eight or nine days in the week so I'd have more time to get it all done!

What else embodies gorgeousness? I believe that it's incredibly important to be authentic. I've met so many influencers in this field who preach one thing on Instagram or YouTube but then don't "walk the walk" on the other side of the camera.

Sure, I enjoy the occasional french fry or pastry, but I always make sure to share those moments with my community -- we are all human after all. I believe that life is about balance and I try to live that philosophy every day.

I also think it's important for mature women to be authentic about their age. I realized this as soon as I started posting videos on my YouTube channel for the Over 50 community. These particular playlists went bananas. I realized that this demographic is being ignored because women are afraid of "aging out."

I like to think more of "aging IN" to the most exciting chapter of our lives. But we have to start with honesty and authenticity. It's all about mindset and dealing with negative beliefs we might harbor about our age!

Creating a vibrant lifestyle isn't about the latest health fads or fitting into the skinniest jeans. It's not even just about yoga or organic makeup or green smoothies. It's about finding a path that fuels every facet of your life with joy.

Once I realized the interconnectedness of everything — humans, animals, and nature — it was easier to make small and then bigger changes with the health of my own body and the whole planet in mind. I believe that every aspect of our life needs to be addressed in terms of longevity and wellness.

I like an integrated approach because every action you take affects your whole life: clean food, optimal nutrition, detoxifying your beauty products and your home. It all intertwines and comes together beautifully.

FOOD HEALS

The most valuable thing we have is our God-given intuition.

I don't believe in a one-size-fits-all approach to wellness -- every person has a different health profile and lifestyle, so trying to cram everyone into the same category wouldn't make any sense.

Listening to your own intuition is way more important than following any self-proclaimed expert or guru.

I try to stick to what evidence-based science currently holds to be true, and what's worked for me. There are too many conflicting opinions on the Internet, so I feel I have a responsibility to my community to stick to only what's been through the filter of peer-reviewed meta-analysis.

I hope that by embarking on a journey of wellness and self-care, we're all able to live our greenest and most gorgeous life.

Sophie Uliano is *New York Times* bestselling author of *Gorgeously Green* and has written three additional books on healthy living.

She was featured on Oprah's *Earth Day* show, where she taught Julia Roberts and Oprah her everyday gorgeously green tips.

Sophie created an accessible doorway for the average person to walk through to live a more holistic way of life. She took green out of the yurt and into the real world. *Good Housekeeping* dubbed Sophie as "A Mary Poppins for the New Millennium."

Learn more at SophieUliano.com.

Food Heals Podcast **Episodes 178, 185, 200 & 212**

CHAPTER 12 – JASON WROBEL: OUT OF THE DARKNESS: MY JOURNEY TO HEALING CLINICAL DEPRESSION

Out of the Darkness: My Journey to Healing Clinical Depression

By: Jason Wrobel

Filed Under:
#theuniverseheals #loveheals #alternativemedicineheals

In 2014, the first season of my TV series was on the *Cooking Channel*, my management team and agents were on fire, and I had my first book deal in the works with the biggest cookbook publisher in the world.

From a career perspective, I was crushing it.

I was a celebrity chef, nutrition expert, and mindfulness practitioner. I had it all. My ego was big and so were my successes.

What I didn't let anyone see was the crippling anxiety and stress from the increased pressures of success, which lead to the dissolution of my long-term partnership in the Spring of that year.

My heart was in deep, writhing pain and I somehow tried to console myself with my material accumulation and more career wins.

I put too much importance on external validation.

Shortly after my breakup, I got an email from one of the producers at the *Cooking Channel* and *Food Network*. She wanted to talk about the first season.

They were cancelling the series due to lack of ratings.

I wanted to cry, scream, throw up, and jump out of my second story window all at once. I couldn't believe how quickly they ended something that took us three years to conceive and launch. It felt like my biggest career win turned to ash in an instant.

Shortly thereafter, I lost the book deal too. They heard about my series getting cancelled and, just like that, yanked their offer in the snap of a finger.

I continued to pitch my book with my agent until we decided on Hay House. In that process, however, my manager dropped me, my book agent dropped me, and I parted ways with my talent agent as well.

Although I had had dark, depressive thoughts in the past, after the emotional heartbreak of all of these situations compounding in such a short period of time, I started to spiral deeper into depression than ever before.

I found myself struggling to get out of bed, digging for any shred of motivation to continue living amidst the rubble of the life I once knew.

And one day in the early summer, I decided I'd had enough.

I wanted to kill myself.

As I started seriously mapping out my suicide, I wanted it to be poetic and meaningful somehow. So I began to write the letter in my mind of exactly what I wanted to say.

It was something about the illusion of the success and the validation we chase. And when it all goes away, we are left with nothing but an empty void.

The most symbolic and meaningful way to kill myself, I figured, would be to stab myself in the stomach with my favorite Japanese chef's knife.

The ultimate final act.

So, I got out of bed on a warm June day, pat my new kittens on the head, and walked into the kitchen. I had a smoothie for breakfast like I usually do, and then I picked up the eight-inch knife and held it to my gut, pressing the tip of the knife into my stomach.

As I closed my eyes and wondered how I would muster the will to do this, a voice other than my own came into my consciousness.

FOOD HEALS

Call it God, spirit guides, angels, ancestors, or divine grace. To this day, I still don't know exactly who or what it was. But it spoke very clearly to me.

The voice said, "Do you really want to die?"

This gave me a moment of serious pause, not only because I acknowledged the presence of this "other" voice, but also because of the nature of the question.

I stood there with the knife in my right hand, staring blankly into nothingness when I got the clarity that changed the course of my fate. I realized that I didn't actually want to die — I just wanted my suffering to end.

And that distinction allowed me to let go of the idea of killing myself and start seeking out real solutions to the suffering.

So I started researching. Like a madman.

I started to research nutrients, neurotransmitters, mindfulness techniques, and alternative treatments for depression and mental illness. I knew that to start healing, I'd need to address my illness from a mental, spiritual, physical, and nutritional level.

The first thing I did was seek out an integrative medicinal doctor to get my blood panels tested and my neurotransmitter function evaluated. I found an incredible doctor in Los Angeles named Dr. Allen Green.

After the test results came back, Dr. Green remarked, "Well, it's no wonder you're depressed. Your results show that most of your primary neurotransmitters are functioning suboptimally."

So we set the course for a host of new supplements, combined with a low-inflammatory diet.

I knew that addressing this illness from the perspective of my mind would also be a huge key and started working for a therapist for the second time in my life (the first time didn't go so well!).

He introduced me to a form of therapy called "somatic experiencing" where we locate trauma in the body and work to release it on both a mental and physical level.

It proved to be deep, potent, and effective for me.

I also started to take my physical fitness a lot more seriously, especially after reading about all the benefits from the additional endorphins, testosterone, and dopamine from doing weight-bearing exercise.

Hitting the gym became medicine for my brain, and I began to feel more calm, confident, and poised.

I also started to address my unexamined, painful, recurring thoughts. In particular, the most potent and persistent thoughts stemmed from the old, deep illusion that "I'm not good enough."

In taking inventory of the frequency and variety of that illusory mental construct, I could see how my mind was simply trying to protect me from the possibility of any future pain.

If I truly believed that I wasn't good enough, then I wouldn't try my best in any aspect of my life. So then, if things failed, I could always default to the fact that I never really put my all into it anyhow.

Recognizing the deepest themes around my pain and their various permutations allowed me to start asking the right questions and creating a more positive, supportive narrative for my life and my sense of self-worth.

Almost five years later, I am doing much better in every aspect of my health, with a few minor exceptions.

To tell you that I'm completely healed from clinical depression would be a fallacy because there are still days when I wake up feeling sad, depressed, and even suicidal. However, they are far less frequent and don't hang around in my headspace for weeks or months at a time like they used to.

All of the tools I've amassed over the last several years have empowered me with new abilities to deal with depressive thoughts when they come up.

It's like I've assembled a superhero belt to which I keep adding cool new tools to help deal with my inner demons.

There is no "destination" for our healing process.

It's an ever-changing, ever-evolving aim in life to be a more whole, complete, and healthy person. As we change and grow, so do our needs, desires, and challenges.

The spirit of being adaptable, flexible, curious, and experimental cannot be downplayed in the quest to live a good, contented, and fulfilled life.

So don't give up, no matter what you're going through.

Whether or not you can see it or feel it in the present moment, everything that is happening in life is ultimately good and to your advantage.

Jason Wrobel is a celebrity chef, television host, bestselling author, and wellness coach.

As the first plant-based chef with a primetime television series, his groundbreaking show *How to Live to 100* taught millions of people how to prepare delicious, organic, and healthy meals at home.

Although he still struggles to love himself sometimes, having four cats and a French Bulldog sure help.

You can follow his journey at JasonWrobel.com.

***Food Heals Podcast* Episodes 7, 10, 15, 79, 172, 173, 174, 175, 176, 237, 244 & 264**

CHAPTER 13 – NICOLE DERSEWEH: THANK YOU, BODY, I LOVE YOU.

Thank You, Body, I Love You.

By: Nicole Derseweh

Filed Under:
#foodheals #loveheals #nutritionheals

I grew up in a household where my dad gifted my mom a thigh master for Christmas.

Each night, my mom would feverishly work in the kitchen creating a well-balanced and healthy meal for our family dinner. Once dinner was served, she would take out a tiny appetizer plate and serve herself a small portion of nonfat cottage cheese and applesauce. Then, she sat at the end of the table to eat this tiny small portion of food while the rest of us enjoyed a full dinner.

The message I received was crystal clear: If you're a woman, the rules are different. You have to give up certain things in order to be loved and accepted.

Cut to my high school years. I was extremely active. I was on the swim team, cheer team, and I was taking private gymnastics coaching. But despite having an athletic body and a healthy lifestyle, things started to change internally.

I can't pinpoint a single moment when it happened, but things started adding up and I felt like something was wrong with me.

Maybe it was my cheer coach pinching the back of my under arm and commenting that I had a lot of fat back there for my age.

Maybe it was the time my dad jiggled my thighs and said I should "cut back" because I was looking "kinda thick," as he handed me the pack of red vines I had requested as a post practice snack.

Maybe it was my 7th grade boyfriend (heavily influenced by his secret collection of Playboy magazines) insisting that I immediately drop and do crunches to make up for tiny indulgences and telling me I'd "be perfect" if I could just lose 10 pounds.

These moments added up to mean one thing: I was not ok.

And if I wanted to be loved and accepted, I needed to lose weight. I thought of my mom and her diets and concluded that the best way for me to lose weight was to eat way less or, even better, not at all.

I started skipping lunch at school — that one was easy because no one really noticed.

Then I started to wake up before the rest of my family to crush a small handful of cereal into a bowl with a splash of milk and place it in the sink to make everyone think I had eaten breakfast.

The only meal I really had to eat was dinner and I could pick my way around that or even get out of it at times by saying I was going to have dinner at a friend's house.

With the level of activity I was carrying out on so few calories, I dropped weight rapidly.

Instead of my dramatic weight loss being met with concern or support, it was complimented — not only by other students, but by the teachers and staff at my school. I was now convinced that I had truly been fat all along and just hadn't realized it. The recognition felt good, so I didn't know how or when to stop losing weight.

I became lethargic in class and light-headed at cheer practice. I was one of the cheerleaders who caught the ones thrown in the air. I remember thinking that I'd never be able to forgive myself if I passed out and someone got hurt because I was too weak to catch them.

But it was too late now.

I just couldn't stop starving myself.

My parents were also divorcing at this time and, while my world was falling apart, what I ate or didn't became one of the few things in my life I felt I could control; it gave me a sense of power and being thin gave me a sense of worth.

FOOD HEALS

I struggled with my eating disorder off and on throughout high school and parts of college. I remember how much I hated feeling weak and exhausted. I wanted to be strong and athletic and perform at my best, but I just couldn't break out of it.

The first sign of relief came in the form of a new boyfriend who liked curves. When he found out I wasn't eating he became very distressed. One night, on a dinner date, I was avoiding eating as usual.

He looked me in the eyes and said, "Fine, then I'm not going to eat until you do."

He playfully whined and complained about how much his stomach hurt, how starving he was, and how he really wished we could both just eat.

I didn't love myself enough to stop the suffering that came from starving, but I did love him enough.

I couldn't stand the idea of his suffering the discomfort of missing even one meal, so I broke. Pretty soon I had eaten an entire burrito just to appease him. Sharing a meal with him made me feel less alone and brought a temporary sense of peace, but on the inside I felt disgusting, fat, and worthless.

Moving forward, I did not withhold food from myself. However, my suffering didn't go away. It just shifted to an internal form of self-loathing.

Hateful thoughts would berate me like a tyrant. This continued for years and I came to believe that, although I had "beaten anorexia" by forcing myself to eat, I may always have "anorexic thoughts."

I didn't think that this mean voice in my head would ever go away.

Here's where my story shifts.

Half a decade later, my family went through several medical crises which turned my world upside down. Both of my grandparents suffered heart attacks and strokes, my grandmother underwent chemotherapy for three forms of cancer, and my dad was diagnosed as pre-diabetic. He was also fighting high cholesterol and blood pressure.

Watching all of this happen to the people I love scared me and made me feel like the same fate was inevitably awaiting my sister and me.

I didn't have to wait as long as I thought.

At 25, I was diagnosed with high blood pressure. At the time I was working out four to five times a week and believed I had a "healthy diet." I was really scared and determined to find a solution so I didn't suffer the same fate as my older family members.

That summer, I went down the information rabbit hole. One documentary led to another and, ultimately, I came to this conclusion: the best way for me to live without fear of these diseases was to go vegan.

To be honest, I was not excited about this information. However, I knew that I wanted to live a quality life of health and vitality. I quickly cut out red meat, then chicken and fish. I adapted slowly over time and, before I knew it, I was one hundred percent vegan.

I felt amazing.

My health was increasing rapidly and I was caring for myself in a bigger way. I felt so empowered by taking hold of my health.

I loved eating in a way that reduced my risk of cancer and heart disease.

I loved that the food choices I made had a positive environmental impact and saved animals.

I loved that I could vote with my dollar and support brands that do good things for people and the planet.

For the first time in my life, eating became a positive thing. Slowly but surely, that self-loathing voice in my head melted away too.

Becoming vegan was the final step in healing my anorexia.

Today, I don't hate myself. I love myself and the choices I make about food. I love eating and sharing this lifestyle with the people around me.

FOOD HEALS

I'm so grateful that I found this lifestyle which has not only saved me from the diseases plaguing my family, but has also healed me from a mental disorder I thought would just plague me for life.

Several years into being vegan, my mental health was strong enough to attempt meditation, something that would have terrified my younger self. It has now become my favorite.

I close my eyes and go through every little part of my body -- toes, ankles, calves, etc. -- and tell it that I love it. I thank my body for being there for me, supporting me, and caring for me. I tell each body part it's beautiful...even my thighs!

Thank you for sharing in my story.

You are perfect just the way you are.

You are beautiful and you are loved.

Thank you for being here on this planet at this time. We need you.

Nicole Derseweh is a world-class vegan chef and YouTube Celebrity with a culinary background from Le Cordon Bleu. You can currently experience her creations at high-end events and exclusive pop-up dinners in and around the Los Angeles area.

Follow her work at Instagram.com/NicoleDerseweh.

Food Heals Podcast **Episodes 149, 172, 173, 174, 175, 177 & 264**

CHAPTER 14 – HAL ELROD: CREATE YOUR OWN MIRACLE

Create Your Own Miracle

By: Hal Elrod

Filed Under:
#thejourneyheals #nutritionheals #theuniverseheals

When I was diagnosed with cancer and given a week to live, it didn't seem fair. After all, I'd already died and been brought back to life three times! But I had faith in my ability to remain positive and heal myself...I'd done it before and I knew I could do it again.

Adversity has been a part of my life from the very beginning.

When I was eight years old, my baby sister Amery tragically died. She'd been born with metatropic dysplasia, an inevitably fatal disease. But instead of letting their grief shut them down, my parents founded a support group for couples who had lost a child. Soon after that, they started selling newspaper subscriptions to raise funds for our local children's hospital.

So at an early age, I was blessed to learn an incredibly valuable lesson: even our darkest moments can be transformed into something positive, and it is up to us to make that choice.

Despite these great early lessons, I lacked direction in high school. I had mediocre grades and I wasn't very athletic or popular.

After graduation, I applied to a company that sold high quality kitchen knives, and during their sales training seminar, I felt a fire light within me. I knew that sales was an opportunity for me to start living closer to my full potential and developing work ethic that had eluded me the first 19 years of my life. By the second day, I vowed to break all of the company's sales records.

But even though I jumped into my sales calls with great enthusiasm, it wasn't quite that easy. I made exactly zero sales. Frustrated, I decided to quit. My boss was blunt in his response,

"You've got two choices: give in to fear and quit, or get back on the horse and be successful."

His tough love changed my mind and I decided to get back on that horse. In the next 10 days, I sold $15,000 worth of knives, breaking the previous all-time record by $3,000.

The company asked me to start speaking at sales conferences.

I thought my life was perfect, but things were about to change in a big way. One night after receiving my first-ever standing ovation at a sales conference, my girlfriend and I were driving home when we were hit head-on by a drunk driver at over 70 miles per hour. My girlfriend was able to avoid major injuries, but I, on the other hand, was practically smashed in half.

When the rescue workers pulled my body from the wreckage, I actually bled out and died. I was clinically dead for six whole minutes before the paramedics brought me back to life.

I had 11 broken bones, a ruptured spleen and severed nerves, and during my surgeries over the next few days, I flatlined two more times.

That's two more times I essentially died!

When I finally woke up from my coma, the doctors told me that I might never walk again. But instead of shutting down or getting depressed, I decided to tackle my recovery with a positive attitude. I established my five-minute rule: when things don't go your way, you can feel bad about it, but only for five minutes. Then, if you can't change it, you have to move on.

With my positive attitude and that five-minute rule driving my recovery, I healed from my accident and returned to the cutlery company. I went right back to setting sales records, but with the encouragement of friends, I soon realized that the story of my accident and recovery might be able to inspire and motivate others.

So, I became a certified life coach and wrote a book, *Taking Life Head On! (The Hal Elrod Story): How To Love The Life You Have While You Create The Life of Your Dreams.*

FOOD HEALS

But wouldn't you know it, life wasn't finished throwing adversity my way.

The global financial crisis hit me and my business hard, and I found myself deep in debt...and even deeper into depression. But I did some serious soul-searching and found a way to lay a positive foundation for every day using a transformative morning routine.

This routine included running, and in 2008 I ran a 52-mile ultramarathon. After my accident, doctors told me I might never walk again, and here I was less than 10 years later, running 52 miles!

My book about the transformative potential of a great morning routine, *The Miracle Morning*, became an international bestseller.

It feels like the story should end there, right? I died in a car crash, miraculously survived and thrived, and found a way to share my insights with the world. But even after all that, the universe had another curveball to throw at me.

In 2016, I woke up one night struggling to breathe. I went to Urgent Care where I was misdiagnosed with pneumonia. They sent me home with some antibiotics and told me to call my doctor if it didn't get better within a few days.

Well, it didn't get any better — in fact, at this point, one of my lungs had collapsed— so I went back to the doctor. I was then diagnosed with acute lymphoblastic leukemia, a rare and aggressive form of cancer that only has a 30% survival rate.

I couldn't believe it. I already lived a healthy life, was getting plenty of exercise, and was on a strict diet of organic foods. How could I have cancer?

It didn't seem fair. I'd already survived so much. I'd already learned so many lessons.

How many more lessons could there be for me to learn?

The doctors told me I needed to start chemotherapy immediately or I would die within a week. As a believer in the power of clean and healthy living, I knew I had to push back.

I told my doctor, one of the top oncologists in the country, that I didn't want to do chemo. I didn't want that poison in my body. I asked him if there was any alternative and he told me that he understood my position but I had a fast-moving type of cancer that wouldn't respond to holistic treatment alone.

"If you don't start chemotherapy immediately, you'll be dead within a week."

I worried that his urgency was just a scare tactic, so I asked for a day to think about it. He agreed but warned me that time was of the essence. So I went home and did a ton of research.

I discovered that my doctor was right: my ultra-rare, ultra-fast form of cancer meant that if I didn't start chemotherapy immediately, I was going to die.

So, begrudgingly, I agreed to the chemo. Even worse, I had to get the strongest chemo drugs in existence, drugs so strong that they would burn through my veins, so they had to be pumped through a tube directly into my artery.

Within three weeks, I lost 25% of my body weight. And, of course, every fiber of my being was screaming out that I shouldn't be putting this kind of poison into my body.

But amazingly, my cancer started moving into remission.

To counter the side effects of the chemotherapy, I embarked on a journey to discover and implement the best holistic practices available. I learned that toxins from chemo build up in your liver, so I dove into a healthy, cancer-healing lifestyle including juicing greens, lymphatic massage, coffee enemas, acupuncture, ozone sauna, food-based supplements, and more.

I threw the holistic kitchen sink at it and I had great results.

Before long, I had beaten cancer and healed my body from chemotherapy.

At each difficult moment in my life, I never doubted that I would recover and truly believe that a positive outlook is behind each one of my miracles.

I fueled my extraordinary faith by putting in extraordinary effort. I fully committed to my goals. Just like I decided I was going to walk again, I decided I was going to beat cancer. I was going to live to be 100 years old, alongside my wife and our two young children.

There simply was no other option.

At the core of all my books and methods is this idea of a positive mindset and an unwavering faith in yourself and your abilities.

Unwavering Faith combined with Extraordinary Effort moves your goals from possible to inevitable.

If you truly maintain faith in your limitless potential and you're willing to put forth the necessary effort over an extended period of time (a.k.a. for as long as it takes), you can create your own miracles.

Hal Elrod is on a mission to elevate the consciousness of humanity, one morning at a time.

As one of the highest rated keynote speakers in America, creator of one of the fastest growing and most engaged online communities in existence, and author of one of the highest rated, bestselling books in the world, *The Miracle Morning*, he is doing exactly that. Check out his new book *The Miracle Equation,* which is in bookstores now.

Learn more at MiracleMorning.com.

***Food Heals Podcast* Episode 259**

CHAPTER 15 – JENNIFER JANSEN: MOMMA GOES VEGAN

Momma Goes Vegan

By: Jennifer Jansen

Filed Under:
#foodheals #loveheals #nutritionheals

I was approximately six months postpartum from having my first child when I distinctly remember making an intellectual and spiritual connection to veganism as I drove home from a long night of waiting tables, listening to the *From the Heart Podcast* hosted by the beautiful and extremely talented yoga girl, Rachel Brathen.

Rachel Brathen has become one of the most successful social media influencers in the yoga world, and I began following her story shortly before she announced her pregnancy with daughter Lea Luna in 2016.

Just two months later, I discovered I was pregnant with a daughter as well.

It seemed meant to be.

I had instantly connected with Rachel's perspective on life and her ability to communicate, lead, and inspire others was contagious. I greatly enjoyed reading her posts about everything yoga and pregnancy-related. I trusted her in the way most millennials do when they feel they have found someone who just 'gets them.'

On this chilly October evening, Rachel interviewed and created impactful conversation with well-known animal activist James Aspey.

In a casually approachable yet effective manner, James described the core of his message as a modern-day Messiah for the animals. He truly spoke from the heart. Most notably, James explained and shed light on the hard truths of the dairy industry.

I had no idea.

Previously, I touted myself as slightly superior to my carnivorous friends because I was a cheese-loving, ice cream fanatic who occasionally indulged in a spicy tuna roll.

Sorta-vegetarian and pescatarian were common words in my vocabulary.

I had no idea the pain and suffering that was occurring due to my continued support of the dairy and fish industries.

Not to mention the environmental impact.

This episode was extraordinary in nature and must have touched many individuals, however, the connection I made as a breastfeeding mother was especially profound and life-changing.

As I drove home, an exhausted new mom struggling to manage the greatest transition in my life to date, I realized how lucky I was to be experiencing motherhood.

I struggled with breastfeeding from the very first day and had resorted to becoming an EP (exclusive pumper) around two months postpartum. It was one of the most emotionally challenging decisions of my life.

I worked so incredibly hard to exclusively pump. My entire life revolved around the pump, my water bottle, and the little plastic bags I obsessively filled, dated, labeled, laid flat to freeze, and stored.

Being hooked up to that machine while my breasts were pulled and prodded to provide my baby girl that liquid gold was both the most challenging and rewarding experience I have ever been through.

Then I made the connection.

Mother cows are forcibly impregnated (being pregnant by choice was hard enough, so I cannot imagine having to do it without giving permission — it is atrocious) and then hooked up to pumping machines after their babies have been ripped away from them.

My heart physically hurts thinking about what it would feel like to have my baby taken from me.

FOOD HEALS

We humans then pump the milk their bodies created in specific response to the pregnancy that we forced them into and the motherhood that is stripped away from them.

Lastly, we steal that milk for own pleasure.

I was in shock.

I have lived in California since I was nine years old and I can confidently and regrettably say, "Happy cows do NOT come from California."

It was also around six months postpartum that I had a terrible bout of mastitis. Mastitis is a nasty infection of the breast tissue. I would not wish this pain on anyone. It is like having the flu while also having incredible pain and soreness in your breasts.

My milk production was forever affected, and I had to quit exclusive pumping eight months after giving birth.

That's how bad it is.

I also learned that dairy cows get mastitis too. And quite often it's because of the high demands of the industry. Again, we inflict such unnecessary pain and suffering for absolutely no reason other than our own personal gain and pleasure.

Why? I knew it wasn't right. I knew there had to be a way that eliminated these awful conditions.

As I write this, my beautiful baby girl is now almost 18 months old, and we are both thriving on a whole food, plant-based vegan diet and lifestyle.

I have not only modified what I eat but also what I wear, the products I clean my house with, and so many other details about my everyday life.

I am so thankful to have listened to that episode and been given the information and encouragement to *follow my heart.*

I transitioned myself over a period of eight months and, when all is said and done, the greatest lesson I learned is kindness and compassion.

JENNIFER JANSEN

When we treat ourselves, the earth, and all other sentient beings with kindness and compassion, only then will positivity and progress prevail.

Making the vegan connection has led me down an incredible path to a life filled with positive energy, love, and vibrance.

I have discovered numerous resources, including the *Food Heals Podcast*, and I just want to shout from the rooftops: #GoVegan!

Jennifer Jansen is a momma bear, living in the 'burbs, trying to live her best life. After transitioning to a vegan lifestyle, Jennifer's life has been forever impacted in the most wonderful way. She spends her days waiting tables, taking care of her daughter, and always searching for new inspiration to share about the vegan movement.

Follow her journey at @the.london.fog.

CHAPTER 16 – JEFF WITZEMAN: HEALING CANCER

Healing Cancer

By: Jeff Witzeman

Filed Under:
#foodheals #loveheals #alternativemedicineheals

"Your lives are going to change forever."

Not exactly the words you want to hear from your doctor when he comes out of surgery with your wife.

"Your wife has a tumor in her bladder. We were not able to get all of the cancer out and it has moved into her bladder wall. The only option is to remove the bladder, followed by chemo and radiation."

Now to back up for a second, let me give you some history.

Kerry, my wife, was only 53 years old.

The options after bladder removal are either a pee bag permanently attached to the side of your body or a neo-bladder made out of intestinal material.

Neither of these were acceptable options to us on any level.

Then we remembered that five years prior, Kerry's sister Dottie had had stage 4 malignant melanoma. After getting a death sentence from doctors in the US, she went to Germany and healed it with natural treatment including hyperthermia (or focused heat), Ozone therapy, and IV nutrients in just 30 days!

Kerry and I called her immediately, and Dottie assured us that we too could go to Germany and have the bladder cancer treated naturally.

At our next appointment, we saw the urologist — the medical doctor with all the specialized training — and as we sat down with him, he smashed our glimmer of hope into pieces.

FOOD HEALS

"You've got a squamous cell carcinoma. It's far too aggressive. There is NO WAY you could ever treat this at an alternative clinic in Germany."

We left feeling dejected and hopeless.

That queasy feeling in your stomach like you're doomed grew unbearable.

But what did we have to lose?

So, we hopped on a plane to Germany and were stunned and amazed by this "natural" treatment in a spa-like setting.

Instead of tearing the body down, they were building it up.

Instead of a glass wall separating us from the receptionist, telling us to sign in and take a seat, we were greeted in a warm room with green smoothies and friendly nurses.

Instead of a bowl full of candy in every oncologist office, we received broth soup.

And, 30 days later, Kerry was cancer free.

No bladder removal. No chemo. No radiation.

Another woman we met while in Germany was not so lucky. After doing everything her doctors in the States told her to do (removing her bladder, getting chemo, and undergoing radiation), she relapsed.

She had come to Germany like we did, hoping for natural treatment to save her where the doctors in the States had failed. But it was too late.

Unfortunately, the woman died from an infection from the shunt that connected to her kidney.

If only the doctors in the U.S. knew!

When we returned home, we immediately wrote to our doctor to tell him about this breakthrough option available for bladder cancer patients.

His response?

No curiosity, no apology, only a brief email saying, "I wish you continued success."

We were floored. And a little more than agitated.

How could this be?

Our Healing Journey Continued

One of the things allopathic western medicine tends to do is treat symptoms. The great revelation of the 21st century is that the human body has the ability to heal itself when given the proper environment.

So how do we create the proper environment?

Where did Kerry's cancer originate?

What was driving the cancer?

These were questions our medical doctors were not interested in exploring, so we started expanding our health team.

First, we found a urologist who was open to natural treatment to monitor Kerry without prescribing drugs as a solution. He was 80 miles away in a small town north of Los Angeles, but worth the drive.

Within three months of returning from Germany, a tiny new growth appeared in Kerry's bladder. And now came the moment of truth: Could we keep the cancer away?

So we found a nutritionist and radically changed our diet to make it more alkaline.
• No refined sugar, gluten, or dairy.
• No farm-raised fish.
• Lots of fruits, vegetables, legumes, and beans.

Smoothies became the new standard.

Next, we had blood and urine samples taken to test for micronutrients, metals, toxins, and hormone levels. Then, we used supplements to balance the body. Probiotics and enzymes were key.

Were we successful?

The answer is a resounding "YES"! By alkalizing the body, we kept cancer at bay.

A couple years later, there was another small recurrence. This time we realized detox was an important part of the recovery process, so we added in an infrared sauna and coffee enemas.

Since then, during a particularly stressful time along with a major tooth infection, another tiny polyp started growing. The infection was treated along with a tooth extraction. We also added cannabis oil into the mix of supplements since it has cancer-killing properties. We really feel like we've got the healthy environment we've always needed and the tests show it with the bladder looking clean.

Cancer-killing is one of our body's beautiful jobs. But we must provide it the right tools. Each year we are adding new tools to our healing toolbox.

More Agitation

What do you do in a world that doesn't care about side effects and toxic treatments?

What do you do about a profession that is quick to prescribe organ and body part removal?

What do you do with a media that loves the money from pharmaceutical advertisers but doesn't hold the medical profession accountable for any corruption?

What do you do with an industry that forces children into long term (2-4 year) chemo protocols even though they are already in remission? (The doctors literally call Child Protective Services to take the children from their parents and put them in foster care for the remainder of intense chemotherapy if the parents refuse).

I can no longer stand by and watch children go through organ failure, brain damage, relapse, and death.

So after making the documentary film *Cancer Can Be Killed* about our experience with natural clinics, I made *Flipping The Script: When Parents Fight Back* and documented parents stopping long-term chemo with the help of attorneys and a new breed of doctors willing to think differently.

Much like what we found, the key to ending childhood cancer is with nutrition, detox, cannabis oil, and testing the body. This archaic notion of bombarding the body with toxins is shockingly misguided.

But when you look at the $1.5 million the industry is getting *per* child, you start to understand why it is so popular.

Healing

So what is needed for healing? What are the factors?

These are the questions we ask all the time and why we listen to the *Food Heals Podcast* and other incredible shows.

Greatly underrated is having a healthy distrust for everyone in power and a deep skepticism of the "experts." Dependency on the "experts" may be the #1 block for people seeking healing.

Everyone's opinion counts and is a valuable member of our team, but ultimately, we are in charge.

We are the ones who know ourselves best. And maybe this leads me to the second most important part of healing for us — taking responsibility. Without it, we are just living on a wish and a prayer, and not a very good one at that.

Everything had to be cleaned up, including the emotional world. We started working with a therapist to repair childhood wounds and reconnect with the powerful adults that we now are.

We also started shopping with farmers we know and trust at the farmer's market to make sure we get the cleanest food possible.

People I have seen die of cancer have missed these two ingredients (emotional healing and clean food) and have given up on taking responsibility. No judgement at all; this is a tall order. But once you get on the healing train and see the results, it's hard to turn back.

Have you seen the change in society over the last five years? (As I write this, I am referring to 2013-2018).

It has been subtle, and toxic medical providers have been doubling down on efforts to control the landscape. But information is spreading faster than they can control it.

There is a growing acceptance that healing is possible through a variety of approaches.

The wrong choice for us would be to expect the medical community to change.

Healing happens when we let go of changing others and take charge of our own journey. Seek those people who can get us to our goals. They are out there.

And the universe is behind us in the quest.

Jeff Witzeman has been an actor, writer, and musician before launching his first award winning film *Cancer Can Be Killed* in 2017. His new film *Flipping The Script* captures never-before-seen footage of children breaking free of an abusive medical system.

Follow his work at CancerCanBeKilled.com.

Food Heals Podcast **Episodes 190 & 258**

CHAPTER 17 – NOOR DAGHISTANI: A PHARMACIST'S AWAKENING

A Pharmacist's Awakening

By: Noor Daghistani

Filed Under:
#foodheals #thejourneyheals #nutritionheals

It was July 2014 and I had just graduated with my Doctorate of Pharmacy.

After a grueling four years of classes, little sleep, lots of coffee, and late nights studying, I was both excited and nervous to begin my post-graduate pharmacy residency training, where I could finally put all the information I had learned into clinical practice.

After all, I went into pharmacy because I wanted to help people heal.

I was just beginning my training at one of the top hospitals in South Florida and couldn't wait to get out there and work with physicians and other healthcare practitioners to serve our patients.

Yet just a few months in, something didn't feel right to me. I watched patients come into the hospital with a long list of medications only to leave with an even longer list.

"How on Earth can you live a happy, healthy life with a list of 10 or more medications you have to take daily?"

I knew medications came loaded with potential side effects too, so there was no way that taking 10 medications in a day could make a person feel great. I had never realized how medications could so easily add up. And the healthcare practitioners defaulted to doling out prescriptions for chronic conditions as if on autopilot.

It was shocking.

During my academic training, I remember my professors briefly mentioning some "non-pharmacological" treatments and barely ever uttered the words "lifestyle changes."

So, I had assumed that physicians and other healthcare providers would be the ones to talk to patients about important lifestyle changes to avoid drugs.

But rarely did this talk happen and when it did, it was very generic, like, "You need to eat healthier and exercise more."

What does that even mean?

Ironically, most healthcare practitioners giving this advice weren't even doing it themselves. Heck...I wasn't either!

Sleeping an average of five hours a night, drinking four cups of coffee, eating tons of junk food, and totally ditching my exercise routine had caught up to me.

A few months into residency, I had gained 20 pounds and started to have stomach pain, heartburn, and indigestion.

My ankle, which had been re-injured during pharmacy school, leaving me with a mild pain that never went away, started to hurt even more. It became difficult to stand on my feet for hours during rounds.

My irritable bowel syndrome symptoms were worse than ever and, to top it all off, at the employee wellness fair my cholesterol levels came back elevated.

I have a family history of high cholesterol, high blood pressure, and diabetes. I was 28 years old and my cholesterol was already high. When I talked to a doctor about it, I was told it wasn't much of a concern.

To hell with that!

I remembered my patients with their long lists of medications and thought, "I don't want that to be my future." I also felt like a hypocrite. How could I walk around and help patients get better if I was not well myself?

Clearly, any advice I gave could not be trusted.

I started thinking, "What can I do now to prevent myself from getting worse? Was there anything I could do to reduce my risk of the diseases that run in my family? What about those lifestyle factors my professors breezed over in class? Could those help?"

So, during the very little free time I had, I started my own research.

The first thing I stumbled upon was a series of TED Talks related to health and nutrition. One really stuck. It was a man who talked about how we eat more meat than we really need to, so his solution involved being what he called a "weekday vegetarian." On Monday-Friday he ate vegetarian meals and on the weekends he'd eat meat.

I liked this idea and thought it sounded like an easy adjustment, so my husband and I became weekday vegetarians.

We were weekday vegetarians for almost a year. I didn't really notice many big changes in my health or weight. What I did notice, however, was that I felt better overall on Monday-Friday and then on the weekends if I had a steak, for example, I would feel heavy and sluggish.

I thought this was all I could do on my own to help reduce my risk of chronic disease. So, I saw a gastrointestinal physician for my digestive symptoms and was placed on a short course of medications to help treat gastritis.

I also saw several physicians about my ankle pain.

The first physician was my primary care doctor who told me to take Advil around the clock for two weeks and see a podiatrist if my ankle didn't get better. I did the Advil for four weeks with no real benefit.

I did physical therapy, which didn't help much either.

I eventually saw the podiatrist who recommended surgery. I refused surgery because I felt that this solution was too extreme. Plus, I was a resident and had no time for that!

At this point, I just accepted that I would have ankle pain for the rest of my life and would have to deal with it.

Meanwhile, my husband started a new job at an online health and wellness company. There, he met a nutritionist who advised him to go fully plant-based for optimal health benefits. He approached me about this change telling me that he was interested in "going vegan."

I had no idea what vegan was and when he told me, I was not thrilled. I prided myself on being a "foodie" and really liked being able to have my steak and seafood on the weekends.

My husband then shared his frustration after trying to convince me to "go vegan" with his co-worker, so she lent him *The Kind Diet* by Alicia Silverstone and told him to have me read it. I read the book and was blown away by the information. It led me to dig deeper and I took a dive into many documentaries including *Forks Over Knives* and *Cowspiracy*.

These documentaries led me to read related books like *The China Study*, *How Not to Die*, and *Eat to Live*.

In pharmacy school, I was taught that chronic illness was hereditary and that diet and lifestyle may help reduce your risk, but you were mostly doomed by your genetics.

Yet the information I was consuming — based on scientific evidence and research — was the total opposite!

Not only could you reduce your risk of chronic diseases, but you could also reverse them in many cases too!

Veganism just made sense. Though, the final deciding factor for me actually wasn't health, it was the animals. Once I witnessed their suffering, thanks to the PETA video *Meet Your Meat*, I no longer wanted any part of an industry that abused our fellow beings.

After making the change to a vegan plant-based diet, I felt amazing.
• I had a newfound energy.
• I no longer had stomach pain or heartburn, and my IBS symptoms subsided.
• My head felt clearer and I felt so much more alive!
• I lost those 20 pounds.
• In just a few short months, my ankle stopped hurting after three straight years of constant pain.
• And my cholesterol levels dropped into the normal range.

I was beyond happy with all the incredible results physically, emotionally, and ethically by going plant-based.

And because of it, I felt a responsibility to let everyone else know too. I started by educating my friends and family and then those patients who were open to the idea of a diet change.

But I felt like this was not enough. I had to get this information out on a larger scale.

So, at my job, I joined the wellness committee and the nutrition committee to work on educating hospital staff and administration about diet and health with the hopes of implementing policy changes to allow for healthier food options for both patients and the staff at my hospital.

I also started a website, a podcast, and YouTube channel so I can educate the public about how our food choices significantly impact our current and future health.

My goal is to empower as many people as I can to take their health into their own hands and help make systematic changes that will improve the health of many.

Food does heal!

Noor Daghistani is a board certified psychiatric pharmacist with a passion for food and wellness. She has made it her goal to educate the public about the physical and mental health benefits of a plant-based diet.

You can find her work at FoodProof.org.

Food Heals Podcast **Episode 211**

CHAPTER 18 – VINCE LIA: WHY ULCERATIVE COLITIS IS THE BEST THING THAT HAPPENED TO ME

Why Ulcerative Colitis is the Best Thing That Happened to Me

By: Vince Lia

Filed Under:
#foodheals #nutritionheals #thejourneyheals

My name is Vince Lia, and I have ulcerative colitis.

You don't hear someone say that very often. In fact, you rarely hear people talking about colitis or other digestive conditions, and it's time we changed that.

But I get it! Who wants to talk about what's going on in the bathroom? It's not exactly *dinner conversation*, but with so many people suffering with this ailment, the more we share, the more we can improve people's lives.

Here's a little background — one day I started to have a sharp pain in my abdomen. I figured it was gas or something I ate, but this pain didn't go away. In fact, it got worse and worse every day.

When the pain got really bad, I went to the Emergency Room not knowing what was going on. When they couldn't figure it out, I was referred to a GI (Gastroenterologist). After a few months of trial and error, my symptoms did not get any better.

What were these symptoms? Bloody diarrhea, urgency to go to the bathroom, and abdominal pain. You get the picture.

I finally had a colonoscopy done and it was revealed that I had ulcerative colitis. I had no idea what this was. My first thought was, "Just give me some meds so I can get rid of this."

Unfortunately, it wasn't going to be that easy.

I was put on a few different medications, but none of them seemed to do the trick.

Because I was having diarrhea and my body wasn't absorbing any nutrients, I started to lose weight — a lot of weight.

Since we're on the subject of food and weight, my diet at the time consisted mostly of meat, chicken, fish, eggs, cheese, yogurt, bread, and rice. That would pretty much sum up almost all of my meals. I was told that fruits and vegetables would upset my stomach and I should avoid them, so that's what I did, and nothing got better.

One day I started talking to a friend who was similarly diagnosed but he started eating more plant-based foods, drinking green juices, and was feeling better. After trying so many different medications and strange diet plans, I figured I might as well give this vegan thing a try and see what happened.

I started with a green juice to kick things off. Keep in mind that my diet was pretty much void of a lot of greens at this time, so I wasn't sure what was going to happen with my digestive system. I started with a green juice since the fiber is removed and without the fiber, vitamins and minerals are quickly absorbed into the body and can aid in the healing process.

To my surprise, my body responded well to the green juice, so I decided to push further. I drank a green juice every morning, and things started to improve. I then gradually started to increase the amount of fruits and veggies in my diet while also removing animal products.

It started with removing milk, cheese, and red meat.

I then stopped eating chicken but held on to fish for a long time. I figured I still needed to consume fish for protein. Once I started doing more research on how much protein we need and the different sources of protein, I stopped eating fish and went completely vegan.

I found that going vegan was actually much easier than I expected. I had already tried so many extreme protocols and diets before going vegan, it wasn't that bad.

I felt better after going vegan and giving up animal products, but I had to be careful. You hear so many people talking about how healthy a vegan diet is, and it can be, when done a certain way.

FOOD HEALS

People go vegan for a variety of issues including health, the environment, and animal rights. However, if your main reason is for health, make sure you read the labels of the food that you're buying. It's easy to fall into the trap of thinking because something is vegan that automatically means it is healthy. You can be a "junk food vegan" and consume a diet that is worse than people who do eat healthy but aren't fully vegan.

This started my journey of researching and learning more about the healing properties in food and learning more about plant-based nutrition.

After reading, researching, and even taking certified plant-based nutrition courses, I felt a strong desire to share this information and help others. It started with posting food pictures on my Facebook and people suggested I start sharing them on Instagram. So I started an account there, as well as a Facebook Page and YouTube channel.

Let me warn you, once you are armed with all this knowledge, it's easy to fall into the trap of wanting to tell everyone what you've learned and why they shouldn't be eating that piece of steak. When I'm in this situation, I remember that I once was eating that steak, piece of chicken, slice of cheese, or cup of yogurt as well.

I put myself in their shoes and slowly introduce them to more information about all the benefits instead of lecturing.

After being diagnosed with ulcerative colitis, I struggled and had some really bad times. I often tell people that the effects of this condition are just as bad mentally and emotionally as they are physically — and you already know all about the physical struggle.

Nutrition is just one component of health; you also need to pay attention to your overall wellness and how it can affect you.

After my initial diagnosis, it was a struggle for me just to go out with friends. I had always worried, "What if I can't find the bathroom in time? What will happen?"

I often just stayed at home, or if I did go out, I struggled with anxiety the whole time. The stress on my body worrying about things prevented my enjoying what I was doing.

I also did my best to cover this up so people weren't aware of what I was going through. That was stressful and exhausting.

All these experiences made me realize that I needed to make my wellness, which includes sleep and stress management too, a priority in my life.

I often get asked if I am still taking some medication, and the answer is yes. I also find those thoughts creeping back into my head that can cause my anxiety to start again. But now I am aware when this is happening and can address it effectively.

Going vegan and educating myself opened up a whole new world of opportunity for me.

I sometimes tell people that being diagnosed with colitis was a blessing. This confuses most people, and you're probably confused yourself. However, I doubt that I would have ever gone vegan or studied food and nutrition like I have if I hadn't been diagnosed with ulcerative colitis.

I now understand the role that food and nutrition play in our lives and how they can impact our health in so many ways. Ulcerative colitis has definitely changed my life, but for the better.

I feel grateful and honored to be part of the Food Heals Nation and have the opportunity to share my story.

Vince Lia is a health coach, speaker, and YouTuber. He is passionate about educating and motivating people about food and nutrition. His goal is to empower everyone to take back their health and live a life Fit From Food.

Download his free ebook *10 Hacks to Eat Healthier* at VinceLia.com/HealthyEatingHacks.

Food Heals Podcast **Episodes 2, 29, 106 & 118**

CHAPTER 19 – CHRISTINA ROULUND: DYING TO BE PRETTY: HEALING FROM BREAST IMPLANT ILLNESS AND PUTTING HEALTH BEFORE VANITY

Dying to Be Pretty:
Healing from Breast Implant Illness and Putting Health Before Vanity

By: Christina Roulund

Filed Under:
#thejourneyheals #loveheals #braveryheals

How I wish I knew then what I know now.

And now that I know what I know, I'm going to fill you in on it so that you don't make the same reckless mistake I did.

Let me start from the very beginning.

I was 23 in 2006. For four years I had wanted to get breast implants. I honestly thought they'd make me happier, more confident, and more attractive.

At this time in my life, from an outsider's perspective, I appeared happy and confident. But inside I was insecure, scared, lost, and unfulfilled in pretty much every area of my life.

I was a mess. I hid it well, though. So in November of 2006, I decided to go ahead and have the procedure to get breast implants.

This is when everything changed. But not right away.

Even with my breast implants, I was still:
• insecure in my body
• picking my body apart in the mirror
• constantly comparing myself to other women
• dieting, binging, and over-exercising to "fix" myself

The implants did nothing to make me feel whole or confident like I had expected. Nothing.

FOOD HEALS

At age 25, I became a certified Personal Trainer through NASM. I was heavily into fitness – obsessed really. I exercised daily, ate really well, and was even an aspiring fitness competitor. And do you know what 99% of fitness competitors have?

You guessed it – breast implants.

In March of 2010, I met John and in July of 2011 we had our son, Connor, and things slowly started to go downhill.

I chalked up the extreme fatigue, moodiness, low libido, and brain fog to just having had a baby, being a new stay-at-home mom, and turning into a bored housewife cooped up in an 800 square foot apartment all day with a newborn.

Plus, I let my healthy diet slip. As a new stay-at-home mom, exercise got put on the back burner too.

I can't even tell you how many arguments John and I got into because I was too tired to go anywhere, I was too tired for sex, I was being a cranky b%*@#, and I was forgetting everything. It's a miracle we're still together.

In September of 2014, I competed in a fitness competition – my second one in a year. This is when things started to go downhill, fast.

In October, I had a lymph node in my right armpit get extremely tender and swollen. At first I thought I pulled something in the gym, but one night I noticed in the bathroom that it was in my armpit. When I stretched the skin, you could actually see what looked like a small olive between my armpit and right breast.

I freaked!

I went to my gynecologist that week to show her. She felt it (ouch) and said something along the lines of, "It feels like a lymph node. If it goes away and then comes back, go see a doctor."

She didn't seem alarmed or concerned at all about it, so I didn't either. About a week later it went away. Sigh of relief. But not for long.

The next month, in December, it returned. I really started to freak out then. I began researching everything I could about lymph nodes and the lymphatic system. Something had to be going on. Lymph nodes don't just flare up for no reason.

At the time, my extreme anxiety and depression bouts and massive hair loss began, and my extreme fatigue, hormonal mood swings, and brain fog accelerated.

I was waking up every morning with so much anxiety and a sick stomach that I'd have to go for a walk around the block and sip on ginger tea as soon as I woke up to calm my body down.

Something I'd never experienced before.

My anxiety and depression was so bad that on December 31st, 2014, as we were out celebrating the new year, I thought to myself, "This will be the last time I celebrate a new year." I felt like I was literally dying — like something was killing me.

I even thought I might have cancer – lymphoma or breast cancer — because I found lumps in my right breast in January 2015 (that's an entirely different story). This is when my passion for detoxing, toxin research, and holistic health sparked.

I was losing so much hair in the shower and in my brush that it shocked me to my core. How was I not bald?

Later in 2015, I was given antibiotics, antiviral medicine, and anxiety pills like they were candy. Nobody ever thought to ask me if I had foreign objects in my body. And I was told "breast implants are safe" back in 2006, so I never even thought to reconsider them.

The antibiotics and antiviral medication did absolutely nothing for my lymph node. Each month it returned. Some months it'd stay for two weeks, some months it'd stay for the entire month.

As I write this, I have been dealing with this issue since 2014 – for over four years!

2015 was by far the worst year of my life. I dealt with:
• brain fog/memory/concentration issues
• extreme fatigue (even though I slept for 10 hours a night)
• anxiety/depression bouts
• hair loss/dry thinning hair
• low/no libido
• tender lymph node in my armpit

- declining/blurry vision
- whacked hormones/moodiness
- cancer scares
- lumps found in my breast

In the following years, I learned how to live with these symptoms. They became a part of me. I forgot what the old me — the real me — felt like or who she was.

In early 2017, a few more symptoms showed up:
- shortness of breath/gasping for air
- ringing in my ears
- achy, stiff hip joint
- hyperthyroid diagnosis

At least 12 symptoms now.

Luckily for me, 2017 is the year I discovered Breast Implant Illness.

What in the world? It turns out that there are tens of thousands of other women who have my exact same story and symptoms.

This discovery was both scary and exciting! I found the root cause.

On August 30, 2018 and four weeks post "explant," here is what has changed:
- My stiff, achy hip joint pain is 100% gone. I used to wake up so stiff – not anymore.
- My shortness of breath is 100% gone. No more gasping for air!
- My skin and hair are so oily and healthy looking (one of the first noticeable things to return).
- I'm not losing much hair in the shower at all.
- My lymph node has not flared up. By this time of the month, it would have already. I had scar tissue wrapped around it – something my surgeon has never seen before.
- I have so much more energy and wake up feeling refreshed and ready to go.
- My brain fog has lifted. I feel like I'm not walking in a cloud.
- My libido is baaaaaack.
- I haven't worn my glasses. My eyes feel less dry and blurry.
- I don't hear loud ringing in my ears at night anymore.

Being able to move without pain, inhale a deep satisfied breath, make it through the day without feeling tired, see and think more clearly, and watch my hair and skin produce oils again has been life-changing.

I'm 35.

Everything I've gone through should not happen to a 30-something.

You can no longer convince me that breast implants are 100% safe.

It's not a coincidence that as soon as I get my implants removed 90% of my symptoms (symptoms I'd struggled with for four years) disappeared.

Not kind of gone – 100% G.O.N.E.

But you may still have some questions about all this.

1. Will everyone experience Breast Implant Illness?
No. It's about 50/50. With this being said, however, everyone will have an immune response. From day one, your body will start fighting them. Over time this will become very taxing for your body – this is a fact.

2. Is it worth taking the chance to see how your body will respond?
No. Not only is it a waste of money, in my opinion, it's not worth the risks.

3. Will they make you happier and more confident?
Who knows? But for me, they did not.

4. What are some simple things you did to help yourself heal and cleanse your body from the toxins and anesthesia after the explanting?
   1. Arnica tablets to help with any bruising and swelling
   2. Probiotics to help my gut and good bacteria flourish
   3. Daily soup with carrots and celery
   4. No added sugar or sweets because they weaken the immune system for hours after consumption
   5. Lots of fresh, organic produce to help with bowel movements and getting in plenty of antioxidants
   6. Rest and relaxation to induce healing and lower cortisol.
   7. Weekly detox baths in bentonite clay, baking soda, and lavender essential oil.

FOOD HEALS

Getting my implants removed was the bravest thing I've ever done.

I'm at a place in my life where I just want to feel healthy, I love my body just as it is, and my health comes first.

Who am I to teach others about health and self-love if I have breast implants? That did not feel aligned or authentic to me.

In March 2017, the FDA finally issued a warning that breast implants cause BIA-ALCL cancer, a cancer of the immune system.

It does not matter if you have silicone or saline implants, they're both toxic.

Saline implants have a silicone shell and can harbor mold, bacteria, and fungus due to faulty valves.

Silicone implants, specifically the cohesive gel, seem to be the worst because they contain more aggressive chemicals.

Both saline and silicone implants have over 40 known toxins, impair the immune system, and release toxins because the shell deteriorates and breaks down over time.

Here's my message to you:
• Breasts do not make you "more womanly" – whatever that means.
• You're beautiful, just as you are.
• You're enough, just as you are.
• You are more than your breast size.
• Having confidence has nothing to do with your looks or breast size.
• You are deserving of love, respect, and recognition — right now — exactly as you are.

It's time to put yourself first.

Fall in love with your body. Respect your body. Embrace your body. Be patient with your body.

No one is supposed to make you happy or tell you you're beautiful – that's something you give yourself.

CHRISTINA ROULUND

Christina Roulund is a devoted wife, a loving mother, and the founder of Size: Happy.

Christina helps women who are sick as a result of their breast implants and educates them about Breast Implant Illness and explanting safely and properly, all while intertwining healing and self-love into the mix.

Follow her healing journey at ChristinasFitness.com/Topics/bii.

Food Heals Podcast Episode 248

CHAPTER 20 – MARINA YANAY–TRINER: FOOD HEALS THE SOUL

Food Heals the Soul

By: Marina Yanay-Triner

Filed Under:
#foodheals #loveheals #meditationheals

When I was in high school, I lost my mother.

She was my best friend. She was the one person I wanted to tell everything to and do everything with. But now, she was gone.

"Don't worry, Marina. Interstitial Cystitis is not a terminal disease. I'm in pain, but I won't die."

It's true, my mother didn't die, but I still lost her.

The person who would go for walks with me, make me food, and listen to me couldn't anymore. Her attention was focused solely on bearing an immeasurable amount of pain.

Interstitial Cystitis is a cruel condition that creates severe bladder pain. My mom had to pee almost every five minutes and spent hours on the toilet, even throughout the night. She just could not focus on anything but surviving.

One day, my mom realized that she had lost the ability to be a mother to me. We both felt the loss.

So, after trying literally everything the doctors recommended, she decided to take healing into her own hands.

My mom switched to a plant-based diet and tried fasting with only water. Although fasting was extremely painful and difficult, after one month of only drinking water, her bladder pain subsided.

She was in awe.

Eight years of severe pain disappeared in just one month.

FOOD HEALS

With the renewed clarity, my mom realized that she no longer wanted just to survive. She wanted to thrive. She deserved to.

She knew that eating plant-based would help her sustain the amazing results of her water fast, so she stuck to it with all her might, and it worked!

This amazing story of transformation inspired me immensely. Not only was it such a gift to get my mother back — and we became even closer — it was also inspiring to learn that the body has the ability to heal itself.

But, my mother was not the only one in need of healing.

While I lost my mother and best friend for about eight years, she had lost me too. I fell into a sexually and emotionally abusive relationship that left me numb and psychologically detached.

I was also just barely surviving in this world.

I lived life from one Post Traumatic Stress Disorder (PTSD) episode to the next, which left me constantly fearful for my safety and well-being.

I lost connection to myself, my friends, and my family, and it was really hard for me to verbalize the emotional pain I was going through.

Not only that, but the deep emotional trauma and stress also caused physical pain. I had severe constipation and horrific premenstrual syndrome (PMS), to the point where I would faint, throw up, and take massive doses of pain killers just to function.

One day, I was driving home from work because my period had come early. The pain grew more and more severe, so I stopped the car on the side of a busy road to rest for a moment.

When I removed my seat belt, I fell straight out of the car and into the busy road, fainting as a result of my severe pain. I was awakened by a screaming woman, who almost ran me over.

That is how bad and scary my PMS got.

When I witnessed my mom's amazing healing story, I had a deep calling to follow in her footsteps. I didn't know at that time that my evolving food choices would impact so much more than just what was on my plate.

I started by removing processed foods from my diet, reading ingredient labels, and gradually transitioned to a fully raw vegan diet.

It wasn't always easy. I definitely clung on to food as a coping mechanism for my deep, hidden pain — I wanted to eat to create a protective barrier between the world and me.

But over time, I was able to let go of the last hurdles for me: dairy and fish. And I gradually transitioned to a whole food, plant-based diet when I learned about the strong scientific support behind these food choices.

This powerful transition helped me heal my terrible constipation and my debilitating PMS. I no longer feared the first day of my period. This alone truly changed my life and gave me so much freedom.

And maybe this sounds like the end of my story.

Although I transitioned to a science-backed, whole food plant-based diet and healed my physical health issues, in reality, it is only the beginning.

Because of my better food choices, I began to connect to myself for the first time after being sexually assaulted.

Instead of wanting to punish myself, I started to want to love myself and bring back my faith in my body and intuition.

I started to realize that my work through food had just begun and that I needed to heal every aspect of my life.

I started to meditate daily. At first, I absolutely hated it and did not understand why on earth anyone would sit cross-legged in silence for 10 minutes.

So many destructive and silly thoughts rushed through my mind.

But I did not give up. I meditated twice a day and started seeing my sleep improve for the first time in years.

I also started working on my mindset around self-love. I started the process of forgiving myself and my body for "failing" to protect me against my assailant.

I made the bold decision to file a complaint at the police station and to meet the person who sexually abused me for three years.

I asked the investigators for the chance to face him and to ask him all the questions I had in the presence of the investigators. Mainly, I wanted to tell him about all the pain he had caused me and to completely release him from my life.

I knew that the likelihood of my official complaint going further than the police station was very low, but I wanted to do this for myself, more than anyone else.

Meeting him was the scariest thing I have ever done. I couldn't sleep, eat, or shower for weeks before that day. But when I did, I bravely spoke my truth and felt a massive wave of pride and trust in my body and my soul rush back into me.

All of these actions were part of a process that is still very much ongoing to heal from my PTSD and to find a connection to myself again.

I discovered a woman who was strong beyond belief, connected, centered, motivated, and in tune with her wisdom and intuition.

I also discovered a girl who is sometimes scared and confused, lost, and in pain.

And I accepted both of these individuals. I accepted that transformation is a gradual process, and with every step, I learn to trust my body more and more.

Most importantly, through this process, I realized that I am powerful and I am not a victim. I no longer wanted to be a victim.

I recognized the part in me that enjoyed and felt the most comfortable with being a victim, and I let her go, because I knew that the price of victimhood is so much more than the reward.

As a victim, I could give myself thousands of excuses to continue feeling pain, self-pity, and self-hatred. When I let go of the victim identity, I felt free, powerful, and in charge of my destiny.

Food heals — absolutely.

It heals so much more than just our physical bodies.

Food can heal the soul because it starts a never-ending journey to really get to the core of us, connect to this core, and share it with others.

Food heals the spirit.

Marina Yanay-Triner went vegan to overcome PTSD and horrible digestion issues. Today, she creates quick, easy, and extremely flavorful recipes on Soul in the Raw and coaches others to transition to a scientifically-supported, whole food, plant-based, high-raw, vegan lifestyle.

Download her free 2-week plant-based meal plan to start your journey at SoulInTheRaw.com.

Food Heals Podcast Episode 150

CHAPTER 21 – KRISTIE REEVES: HEALING OUR BODY BY HEALING OUR SOUL

Healing Our Body by Healing Our Soul

By: Kristie Reeves

Filed Under:
#foodheals #spiritheals #alternativemedicineheals

"Illness and health are singular concepts, since they refer to a human state or condition and not, as is fashionable in today's usage, to organs or parts of the body. The body is never ill or healthy, for it does no more than express messages from our consciousness."

Dr. Ruediger Dahlke & Thorwald Detleffson, *The Healing Power of Illness*

Have you heard the term "psychosomatic medicine"?

Have you heard the body described as "the mirror of our soul"?

Are you aware that your mind, emotions, and body are connected?

Well, then let me tell you my story!

It all started in high school. I was one of those kids who would get a cold when someone else sneezed just three feet away from me. We'd have swimming lessons during the cold German winters — not enough time to dry our hair because we had to run off to our next class — and the following day, I'd wake up with a sore throat.

Around that time, my mother started reading *The Healing Power of Illness,* a 384-page book outlining the connection between illness and our emotions. She'd hand me the book saying, "You should take a look at what your recurring colds mean."

"Mum! Really!?"

As an 18-year-old teenager, enjoying time with friends and taking ballet classes after a long day at school was so much more exciting than reading up about the psychosomatics of my colds and uncovering the hidden emotions and patterns that caused them.

Right?

A couple of years later, doctors diagnosed me with neurodermatitis, a neurological disorder involving chronic itching and scratching.

If you have never known anyone with neurodermatitis, let me tell you, it sucks!

My legs and arms were covered with rashes. The itching got so bad that I'd constantly wake up at night. I'd wrap my arms and legs with wet towels in order to go back to sleep. The damp towels would allow me to sleep for a couple of hours until the itching became so strong that I'd awake again.

I was studying ballet full time but was not able to get a good night of sleep, and having to show up early at the dance studio was starting to take a toll on my emotional health.

I was at the end of my rope.

My most precious thing, ballet, had become torture; it was unbearable to wear my pink tights. I was like a red hot tamale leaping through the air. With each movement, I wanted to turn this graceful dance into a one woman wrestling match with my skin in hopes of destroying the enemy with a flash scratch attack.

My medical doctors had no idea how to help me, so I sought out a dermatologist. She took one quick look at the rashes, told me it was neurodermatitis, and gave me a prescription for cortisone cream.

I asked, "Hold on, is there anything else I can take?"

"No, only cortisone will help you!"

"What about nutrition?" (I had somehow heard that nutrition could help with this).

"No, there's nothing you can do about this but apply the prescriptive cream."

"Well, how long will it last?"

"The rest of your life."

"Wow, is that all? This is terrible."

Luckily, that disappointing answer got me so angry that I walked out of her office and tore up the prescription — right in front of the pharmacy next door! I had to find another way!

Through one of my mum's friends, I found a naturopathic doctor. At my first visit, the ND discovered that I had high levels of pentachlorophenol in my body, a chemical that is used as a preservative in leather as well as wood.

"Ahhaa!"

My school had just gotten new hardwood flooring, so I had an idea. With my ballet friends standing guard, I secretly sliced a piece of wood from the floor, sneaked it out of school undetected, and gave it to my ND. (Go Rebel Hearts!) She then ran a test and confirmed: the pentachlorophenol was indeed from this crappy excuse for a dance floor.

"I knew it!"

She told me that my kidneys were on overload trying the eliminate the toxin, so my body had kicked up its defense mechanisms and was pushing out the toxins through my skin.

This was the reason for the irritating rashes — NOT what the dermatologist had diagnosed.

"Eat it, neurodermatitis!"

On top of it all, the toxins had affected my digestive system, causing elevated levels of candida and allergic reactions to foods, especially to wheat and dairy (I wasn't yet vegan at that time).

My ND went on to tell me that using the cortisone cream would have actually pushed the toxins back into my body, most likely becoming the cause for more serious health issues.

(I am still friends with this naturopath! She's awesome!)

"Wow, lucky me for being so angry at that downer dermatologist."

My ND also used frequency technology, bioresonance therapy to be exact, to support my body's detoxification process. Now, if you haven't heard of frequency technology, let me tell you, it is amazing!

Our body has its own own electromagnetic frequency patterns. When these patterns slip out of alignment, we become sick. During a bioresonance therapy session, energy wavelengths are sent into the cells of the body, returning our cellular frequencies to their natural state.

This process worked. I was literally symptom-free within six weeks. Uff, I was healed. Finally!

I did a ballerina kick in the air and went right back to my old life.

The interesting thing though was that shortly after being declared "cured," the symptoms came back even though nothing was wrong with me on the physical level. Tests came back clear, the pentachlorophenol was completely out of my body, and we were in a different studio without that sucky floor.

"Dang it! Now what's going on?"

I was eating healthy, took my supplements, and yet the symptoms remained.

That's when I remembered.

"Mum, where is that book you showed me a couple of years ago? You know, the one about illness and emotions. I am finally ready to read it!"

And then it clicked.

I had been going to a school that made me unhappy.

I had been pushing myself to finish the program because what you start, you must finish, right?

I had been neglecting my own emotional well-being in order to achieve a goal that wasn't in alignment with me in the first place.

"Darn stubbornness!"

My body had been giving me messages. From colds and stomach flus, to snowboarding accidents and shin splints, my body had been talking to me all along.

But because of fear, I had ignored that voice until the symptoms became so bad that I was forced to listen.

My body had been saying: "Hey, pay attention. You're not living the life you want to live. Stop compromising and do what makes you happy."

"Ahhhh…that's what it was!"

For quite some time, I had gone against my better judgement, fearing that if I followed my truth I'd be lost. Part of me wanted to finish my degree and part of me wanted to quit. I resented the school I was attending, but it was the only German school that offered the program.

What was I going to do? I had come to a point where the pain of continuing was more painful than the fear of change.

They say, "Jump, and the net will appear."

And so I did.

I did a grand jeté (that's a ballet term for a big leap) and the net appeared in the form of a former teacher who offered to mentor me, so I could finish my degree via a long distance program.

"YAY!"

Within two weeks of quitting, the symptoms disappeared and never came back. I had been looking for a solution on the physical level without success, while the answer was there all along on the emotional level.

Our body is the mirror of our soul. It speaks to us.

Whenever we are experiencing physical symptoms, we need to ask our body: "What is it you want to tell me?"

FOOD HEALS

Physical symptoms mean that we are being asked to make a change.

Change our lifestyle, change our job, or change the place where we live. Uncover subconscious patterns, emotions, and beliefs, and ask yourself what needs to be healed, shifted, or transformed.

What it is that you really want?

Remember that we are spiritual beings having a human experience. Therefore, in order to fully heal, we need healing to take place on all levels — body, mind, spirit, and soul.

If we take care of our body, but neglect looking at our beliefs and emotional patterns, we deny ourselves our soul's calling and neglect the majority of who we are.

If we live a spiritual lifestyle but continue to feed our body junk food and surround ourselves with toxic chemicals, we neglect to take care of the vessel that hosts our soul.

True healing happens when we address and unify all aspects of who we are.

The ability for our body to heal itself is absolutely miraculous if we provide the right environment, both physically and emotionally.

Don't make the mistake that I did.

Ask yourself every day, "Am I doing what I love doing? Am I following my heart?"

Whenever a symptom comes up, ask your body, "What is it you're trying to tell me? What change can I implement to realign myself with my truth so that I can release you from having to create a physical symptom to make me pay attention?"

A simple soul request can manifest itself into a slew of physical issues. By just paying attention, we can avoid years of unnecessary suffering.

I am sharing my story with you so that you know:

You are NOT the victim of your circumstances.

You are a magical being who has the ability to step into abundant health. Your body is a miracle and it has a powerful potential to heal itself.

Are you ready to listen? The choice is yours!

Kristie Reeves has worked as a filmmaker, author, speaker, and host of *Rebel Hearts with Kristie Reeves*.

She is the CEO of Songlines Film. With her partner Jivananda, Kristie co-founded AvaitriA Akashic Academy to empower the Indigo warriors of the world.

See her work at KristieReeves.com.

***Food Heals Podcast* Episodes 107 & 147**

CHAPTER 22 – JJ FLIZANES: CREATING A FOOD LOVE AFFAIR

Creating a Food Love Affair

By: JJ Flizanes

Filed Under:
#foodheals #loveheals #thejourneyheals

I started my first diet when I was in junior high school. Back then I had no idea how the biochemistry of food affected my body or my cravings, so I battled with body shame and "losing those extra 10 pounds" for most of my life.

Growing up Greek and Italian, with lots of homemade cooking, I loved being part of a family with cherished food festivals. I have always loved food, and we often celebrated with huge spreads of delicacies.

In 1996 when I became a personal trainer, I started to learn the science of food and how it affects the body and weight gain.

After years of calorie counting and fad diets, I realized that I had made food "the enemy." It had lost its joy and become something to avoid or critically label as "bad" or "good."

We, as a society, have lost touch with our relationship to what we put on our plates. With at least three opportunities every day to practice receiving the transfer of energy from our meals to our cells, eating has become a source of confusion and conflict rather than a delightful pleasure.

The lack of respect and abuse of food is one of the reasons why our health is rapidly declining. For some of us, the concept of doing anything except ordering in or going out seems like too much work. Our lives are too busy to slow down and prepare a home-cooked meal.

Something intuitively felt very wrong about this approach that, like so many of us, I had also fallen into.

So I started to examine my relationship with food.

FOOD HEALS

I wanted to change my behavior and influence both my clients and loved ones to create a food love affair. Who doesn't love a good love affair?

But in order to achieve it, we have to have a deep, meaningful, respectful, and loving relationship with what we put in our bodies.

In cultures throughout history, hunting, gathering, raising, and preparing foods was an honored and respected daily ritual. People were in tune with the abundance of each season and the diversity that the earth provided throughout the year.

Modern living has taken away our attention to this. I got "too busy" to cook.

So, to heal my obsession with dieting and calorie counting, I began treating food as my new lover. Rather than making it the enemy, I wanted to fall in love.

My first experience with the "A Food Love Affair" was in 2003 when I was living in New York City. A friend and I were studying Anatomy for a personal training exam, so she would come over for dinner several times a month.

To contribute to the meal, she would stop off at the local fruit and veggie cart below my apartment and pick something up for dessert. One day, she bought a cantaloupe.

Now, I like cantaloupe, but it's not my favorite fruit in the world. When she excitedly presented it to me, her energy was so focused on the beauty, smell, and taste of what this cantaloupe would offer, that you would think she were having an orgasm.

At first, I thought she was a bit nuts because it was just a cantaloupe. I get excited about cookies and cakes but not really about fruit.

But her energy was infectious, and I noticed how much I really did enjoy the cantaloupe and how fulfilling it was to eat it for dessert. I was certain it was because of the love and connection she infused into it before we ate it.

Her reaction changed how I looked at it and, thus, my experience of it as well.

As another example that I experienced this same transformational joy, I bought two fruit trees around Valentine's Day one year as I was getting ready to move, thinking the trees would be a great addition to my future garden.

But after over three years of growth, the trees bore no fruit or leaves.

Until one day, I noticed a lone nectarine — the only fruit that had ever appeared — and I can't tell you how excited I was to eat it! I imagined the tastes prior to actually eating it and visualized savoring every single bite.

I had never been so excited about a piece of fruit in my life! I might have had an orgasm as I ate it, just like my friend with the cantaloupe.

This is "Creating a Food Love Affair."

I noticed how the positive energy towards food affected how much I ate, when I got full, and how I enjoyed it.

But there was still some more research and testing to do with some of those foods that created cravings or that I still tended to overeat when feeling emotional or stressed out. I was starting to notice other symptoms of digestive issues, congestion, and constipation.

So, in 2008, I decided to go gluten-free as a trial. I had suffered from painful bloating but always attributed to my menstrual cycle. After six days of being completely off gluten, I released 10 pounds. I was shocked!

I was definitely not starving myself or on a low-calorie plan, so I knew I was onto something. Going gluten-free really easy for me when I saw the effects of taking it out of my diet.

The bigger challenge was going to be dairy.

Three years later — after resisting the fact that I knew food was the reason for my congestion every night before bed — I decided to eliminate dairy for a few weeks. Within five days, eating only some tasty substitutes, I no longer had a craving for dairy and eliminated my nightly congestion.

Dairy was harder to release and replace than gluten but recipes and substitutes have come a long way. They are pretty amazing and make dairy-free quite easy.

Now this may seem like I have made gluten and dairy the enemy because now I have restricted them from my diet. And while I am 99% off both of those foods, I do occasionally have them under certain circumstances and when the effects, if any, are worth it.

Removing gluten and dairy forced me to become creative and experiment in making favorite comfort foods that I crave in a healthier way.

My love affair is as strong today as it's ever been. I even started a video podcast cooking show to inspire others to start making these easy shifts in their meals.

In 2011, I held a two-day workshop based on my book *Fit 2 Love* and did another experiment around creating a food love affair.

At the shared meal each day, as the participants gathered around the table with menus in hand, I focused the group's attention on each individual ingredient and how it affects our bodies.

As we went down the list, it was obvious that certain foods were better known for their healthy attributes, but there were a few ingredients that stumped the crowd. As we completed the list of ingredients and blessed the food, the energy in the room changed.

What happened next was a surprise, but it confirms the power we have to connect with our food in a way that transforms the experience. I watched a room full of women who tend to overeat, enjoy a smaller portion (by their choice, not mine) and be completely full and satisfied.

When I later got my hands on a book (*Earthing* by Clint Ober) that explained our connection to the Earth and the positive charge it has on your body to heal pain, reduce inflammation, and help with sleep, it confirmed what I was experiencing and witnessing in others. It proved my theories around "Creating a Food Love Affair."

My food love affair now allows me to look at food and eating as a welcome challenge to create anything I want but in a healthier way. I never feel restricted and I usually get inspired to play in the kitchen and create something amazing that everyone loves and has no idea is actually healthy!

I now treat my dining experience as sacred.

Slowing down and enjoying what is on my plate means chewing it thoroughly, savoring the flavors, feeling the textures, and enjoying the pleasures of each bite.

And because of the change in my relationship with food, it has also allowed me to attract more deep and meaningful relationships and love in my life.

My practice of "Creating a Food Love Affair" has even helped me attract my perfect love partner who now enjoys both a love affair with me and with food.

JJ Flizanes is an Empowerment Strategist and the host of several podcasts including *Fit 2 Love* and *Spirit, Purpose & Energy*.

Her newest book, *The Invisible Fitness Formula: 5 Secrets to Release Weight and End Body Shame,* debuted at #2 on the Amazon bestseller list for Women's Health.

Get a free copy of the book at JJFlizanes.com/Book.

***Food Heals Podcast* Episodes 25, 37, 56, 60, 64, 167, 169, 171, 216, 222, 226, 244, 253 & 282**

CHAPTER 23 – SUZY HARDY: NEEDLES AND TEARS

Needles and Tears

By: Suzy Hardy

Filed Under:
#thejourneyheals #alternativemedicineheals #energyheals

It happened near the commons of my high school. Built in the 70s, the building had areas for each grade — we called them "wells" — where kids could hang out in between classes.

It was here where the cheerleading incident happened that would affect the rest of my life.

I'm fairly tall for a woman. At 5'7", my mom told me that my baby height predicted I would be 5'9". So, I guess I was supposed to be taller. But being 5'7" on this squad was actually really tall because most of my teammates were a lot shorter.

This automatically made me one of the two people needed to form a "base" for when we put a smaller girl up into a pyramid. It's quite a process. First, we would get the smallest girl halfway up, with her feet at our collarbones. Then, we would use all our force to push her above our heads, leaning in so that the three of us formed a triangle and the weight of her body was distributed.

This particular day was nothing special. We had been practicing our formations together for a while and had even won some cheer competitions, so we were good at pyramids.

I don't know how it happened, and, according to the laws of physics, it shouldn't have. But the girl we lifted somehow went from standing up to doing the splits above us. It forced my arms back behind my head and tweaked my lower back.

That was it. No drama. No big deal.

We got her down and I walked it off, thinking I had a mild sprain, just like I had experienced in soccer, ballet, and lacrosse.

FOOD HEALS

I was wrong.

The little tweak in my lower back slowly got worse, but I was 16 years old and continued to live life. After a few weeks, however, when it hadn't gone away, I went to the chiropractor. He adjusted my bones and gave me muscle stimulation to try and release the knot in my back.

A month after that, I went to the doctor because the knot had sprouted friends, and I now had pain above the area that originally hurt too. The doctor just told me to take Advil.

Advil did not do anything for me.

At the time I didn't know it, but my body was trying to talk to me, "Help me! I'm injured! Oh, you are going to ignore me? Ok, watch this!"

When you have an injury, your soft tissue actually hardens in an effort to prevent mobility and enable healing, sort of like a self-imposed body cast. When this is in your back, it can be devastating. Six months after this incident in the commons, I was in constant back pain and could not get up out of a chair without pushing myself up like an old lady.

I went from being an athlete to being immobilized.

Luckily for me, but unfortunately for him, my cousin injured his hand in football around this time. One of his teammates just happened to have a mother who was an acupuncturist. I had a fear of needles but was in so much pain that I was willing to try anything. By this time I had also developed sciatica (back pain caused by a problem with the sciatic nerve in the lower back that spreads to the hip, buttocks, and legs), which was extremely painful and affected me every waking moment.

Reluctantly, I went to get needled.

Dr. Cho was a kind lady who explained the process of how the acupuncture would work: get my stuck chi to move, enabling the muscles to relax and allow my body to finally heal. Later I would learn the needles also innervate muscles that are stuck. My body was all locked up, and it was time to let it all go.

SUZY HARDY

I did not need to believe in this to work. It worked all on its own.

After the doctor and chiropractor could not help me at all, the combination of acupuncture and massage healed my injury in six weeks.

The pain got worse before it got better, but I learned later that this is called a healing crisis and happens when your body is allowed to heal itself.

I went back to cheerleading and sports but would always have to monitor my back. If I got stressed, it could spasm. If I went skiing in very cold weather, it would spasm. This part of my back was a weak point in my system that was a part of me now and I would have to nurture it to keep it happy.

When I moved on from high school and got to college at UC Berkeley, I had to find a new acupuncturist. Luckily, there was a plethora around the Bay Area.

There was a particular time when I was studying for midterms, had come down with a cold, and my back was bothering me. My new acupuncturist heard me sniffle and said, "Want me to make that go away?"

"Can you do that?" I responded.

"Turn over. We will put needles in your front to battle the cold."

I was floored when the next day my cold seemed to have subsided. I was even more fascinated by this healing modality when, during another session, the doctor was working on my back and I began to cry uncontrollably.

I have never been one to hold back my emotions, but this seemed strange to me. Nothing had happened in that moment, but all of a sudden, I couldn't stop balling.

"The body holds emotion. We are moving energy and moving any emotions you may have stored there. The low back relates to the first few chakras that correlates to family, home, and stability."

I was a Psychology major. I had always thought psychosomatic illness was B.S., but that was not what he was talking about. He was talking about body-mind connection, and that there is, in fact, no separation.

Your emotions occur in your brain but they affect every part of your body, and you can store certain emotions or even trauma in certain zones of the body.

This was fascinating!

But I wouldn't learn more about this until I moved to Los Angeles and decided to become a massage therapist while I pursued an acting career.

In massage school, where we worked on each other for hours a day, I was the first to ball my eyes out on the massage table. I was releasing years of stored emotion and it felt amazing.

I studied energy work as well and developed a private practice healing others just like I had been healed.

Although I have a hard time believing everything in life happens for a reason, I do believe that I was meant to become a healer and I had to be injured in order to follow that path.

It enabled me to have compassion for others going through body pain when they are told "there is nothing else we can do for you."

The body has an amazing capacity to heal itself.

All you have to do is get out of the way and give it the tools to do so.

I know this because I've lived it over and over again since I was 16.

Suzy is owner of CBD Fountain (a hemp CBD company in Oregon), a regular co-host of the *Food Heals Podcast*, and a retired massage therapist. She is passionate about natural healing.

Follow her work at CBDFountain.com.

CHAPTER 24 – ELANA LAVINE: BLINDLY FOLLOWING THE HEALTHCARE SYSTEM

Blindly Following the Healthcare System

By: Elana Lavine

Filed Under:
#foodheals #alternativemedicineheals #thejourneyheals

I'm sorry, folks.

We don't get a one-time-only redo card.

There is no special time machine to remake our past with a better outcome.

All we can do is take what we have learned, implement it for ourselves, pay it forward, and share with the world.

If my story has the ability to make even *one person* hesitate before falling down the same rabbit hole as I did, then I get back a little bit of what was taken.

I was a product of the healthcare system.

At the age of 16, my intuition was being suppressed and overshadowed by the looming medical professionals who spewed their "better" approach to my chronic acid reflux and anemia.

The concept of holistic or alternative options was not part of the game plan. Even if I had questions, they always had a rebuttal that I couldn't seem to counter.

I wasn't educated about other options, *yet*.

So as a teenager, I went on Nexium for acid reflux, Lexapro for anxiety, and Xanax for "just in case" scenarios. This all came at a pivotal point in my life.

Instead of deciphering the root cause of my issues, I was given masks in the form of pills. As a late teen and early adult, I had more pills bouncing around in my purse than most should ever have in their lifetime.

Looking back, that wasn't even the worst part.

Where I grew up, this was normal. Kids swapped pills and boasted about which medications they were on — this was our culture, our generation.

It wouldn't be until later, until after the damage was done, that I took a stand.

Going on Nexium was a crutch and it taught me nothing about important diet and lifestyle changes. I just wanted to be a normal college student, binge drinking while eating cheese pizza before bed. So I did!

I kept taking my prescriptions to "counter the effects" without paying too much attention to the harm alcohol had. For someone with serious acid reflux, the damage from what I was doing to myself was piling up big time.

Eating a large McDonald's fries every day for lunch and going to work out the next day became a pattern.

Why stop unhealthy behavior patterns if a pill can help mask my symptoms?

Have a flare-up? Take an extra dose.

Crutches are an escape from reality.

Acid reflux is no joke. Anxiety is no joke. Anything that you could be prescribed medication for is no joke.

After a period of time, I wondered why my body continued to feel worse. I would feed it the occasional organic apples, natural supplements, and workouts.

So why was my body doing nothing to fix itself?

Why wasn't the purple pill healing me?

I didn't realize that in order to heal myself, I needed to dive in head first and take away the crutches.

That's when I "awoke."

Sadly, it took three endoscopies, years of prescription drug abuse, and serious, barely breathing flare-ups, but I finally woke up.

I knew there had to be a better way. So, I began to read more and listen more. I went on life-changing retreats and experimented with a plethora of natural supplements while seeking out new naturopaths. I became a guinea pig, not just for myself, but for those in my same situation.

I wanted others to know what I began to unravel. That not all medical professionals are created equal. There are different schools of thought and there are different forms of healing, if we give them the chance.

It's not "my way or the highway" when it comes to health.

Will I ever be 100% there? Probably not, but my eyes are open. My lifestyle, my diet, and my mindset have dramatically shifted.

I don't take any prescribed medication anymore and I've found alternative options that work for me.

I do have the occasional flare-ups, but now at least I know what causes them.

I do have the occasional anxiety bouts, but now at least I am armed with tools to manage them.

Ebbs and flows are a part of life. My diet isn't always perfect, my mind isn't always clear, but I'm no longer avoiding my body's distress signals.

Thankfully, I have seen a shift in our culture since my high school days. Other people are beginning to wake up and question things too. Celebrities are weighing in more positively, and the media has begun to endorse alternative options more than Big Pharma.

I do believe there is a time and a place for Western medicine, but we must do our homework. We can't follow it blindly.

I have Western, Eastern, and everything in between to keep myself well-rounded.

Teens (and adults) in the same boat I was should be educated more thoroughly on all the options. They should be taught what acid reflux is and how it could impact them in the future if left untreated or aggravated with prescriptions.

What have I learned to specifically combat acid reflux?

To start, eat an anti-inflammatory diet with natural supplements.

For anxiety, some of my favorite options are yoga, meditation, hiking, therapy, and even boxing.

One lifesaver for me was finding and designating certain friends I can trust and turn to when needed. If they are true friends, they will understand and never think of it as a burden to be there for you.

Before blindly accepting Big Pharma, create healthy habits for your present and future.

A few books to read to get more education include *Medical Medium, Skinny Bitch, The Kind Diet*, and *In Defense of Food*.

When it comes to supplements, I recommend Enzymedica Acid Soothe, Now Papaya Enzymes, Detoxosode Metals (with the guidance of a naturopath), and Solaray HCL with Pepsin at every meal.

If you are someone who loves Tums, swap them for Country Life Acid Rescue.

In my fridge and pantry I love to keep Traditional Medicine fennel tea, Kite Hill unsweetened yogurt, fresh papaya, alkaline water, Four Sigmatic mushroom tea, aloe vera leaf juice, bananas, avocados, and green vegetables.

A go-to meal for when I have a flare-up or to keep homeostasis is steamed green vegetables with purple sweet potatoes, fresh avocado, and coconut aminos.

For healing the gut, one of the best-kept secrets that I wish I knew as a teenager is 16 ounces of straight celery juice on an empty stomach every morning. Check out the Medical Medium to get an in-depth understanding as to why.

Today, I am no longer the person sitting idly by and letting others make decisions for me.

Instead, I empower myself on a daily basis to take my health into my own hands. I know that by giving my body what it needs — whether food, supplements, or celery juice — that my body will heal itself.

It works every time. *Food Heals*, folks.

After years of struggling with the healthcare system, Elana Lavine became a wellness advocate dedicated to enlightening individuals on what blindly following the masses can do to one's health.

She shares sustainable businesses, alternative health options, and physical activities on her website and social media accounts.

Follow her journey at Klean-Slate.com.

Food Heals Podcast **Episodes 120 & 218**

CHAPTER 25 – CATHARINE ARNSTON: LOVE AND ALGAE CAN HEAL THE WORLD

Love and Algae Can Heal the World

By: Catharine Arnston

Filed Under:
#foodheals #alternativemedicineheals #thejourneyheals

"I have breast cancer."

Those words from my younger sister stopped me in my tracks. In an instant, my world came to a crashing halt.

How could this be true?

How could this vibrant, young mother of two with a healthy diet and active lifestyle get breast cancer?

You can't control what life throws at you but you can control how you react to it. So as soon as my sister told me she had breast cancer, I knew I wanted to help her. I didn't know how but I was determined to support her in any way I could.

The journey would transform us both.

My sister met with her oncologist who advised her to change her diet to alkaline. The oncologist didn't explain what an alkaline diet was or why it would help, so my sister called me for help.

I was a highly stressed corporate executive with an MBA doing international economic development and my knowledge of nutrition was about as deep as my knowledge of space travel. In other words, zero.

But my love for my sister and my research skills run deep.

As I dug into the science of alkaline foods, I discovered thousands of scientific articles about the healing properties of plants.

I was dizzy with disbelief that something so powerful was so unknown to consumers.

It turns out that the phytonutrients, chlorophyll, bioavailable vitamins and minerals, and the alkaline pH of plants have been documented for centuries. They are all well-known in holistic medicine for their soothing, cleansing, and healing effects on the body.

No wonder my sister's oncologist instructed her to adopt an alkaline diet! Her immune system clearly needed this kind of nutritional support to get her safely through cancer and chemotherapy.

And it did.

Not only has my sister celebrated 10 years cancer-free, she has a new life.

And so do I.

My love for my sister led me to discover my mission in life.

After a year of researching alkaline and plant-based foods, I wanted to share my knowledge with more people so I could help them too.

But how?

I had no nutritional training. I had no idea where to even start. For inspiration, I signed up for a one-day self-help seminar in New York City appropriately called "You Can Heal Your Life" with Louise Hay.

At the event I learned about the Institute for Integrative Nutrition (IIN), and something clicked. I contacted IIN, was accepted, and enrolled within the week.

My transition out of the corporate world and into the plant-based nutrition world was now official. There was no turning back. I had no idea how I would support myself financially while I was in school, nor did I know what I would do once I graduated.

But my gut said do it!

My family and friends thought I had lost my mind or was having a midlife crisis. And while I was nervous and anxious about the future, I was determined to stay the course.

FOOD HEALS

John Wayne nailed it when he said, "Courage is being scared to death but saddling up anyway."

Attending IIN was mind-blowing. I'd never met so many people passionate about plant-based nutrition in my life. We sang, we hugged, we laughed, we cried. Quite a difference from my 25-year corporate career.

Graduation was bitter sweet. What had I gotten myself into? I had no job, no income, and certainly no Plan B.

Trying hard not to hit the panic button, I decided to put what I had learned to use by creating a plant-based curriculum. For the next year, I gave plant-based workshops at corporations, hospitals, and offices interested in wellness.

I became known as the "Not-Eat Nutritionist" because a lot of my lecture content advised people what "not" to eat (acidic foods like dairy, processed foods, sugar, etc.).

This moniker evolved into the Naughty Nutritionist because when you say "Not-Eat Nutritionist," it sounded like "Naughty Nutritionist"!

At my workshops, I learned that virtually everyone wants to eat more greens but they either don't have time to prepare them or don't like the taste of them. That's when I had my next epiphany.

To help people be healthier with plant-based nutrition, I needed to find something that:
• provided alkaline, healing benefits of greens
• was a whole food
• was unprocessed
• was rich in chlorophyll and phytonutrients
• was fast and easy
• didn't require any cooking or cleaning
• didn't taste "green"

Impossible right?

The answer hit me out of the blue.

It was algae.

Yes, algae.

CATHARINE ARNSTON

It may be new to you, but algae is actually mother nature's original food and the first life on earth. Humans only showed up the planet 800 million years ago. Algae beat us by three billion years and is still here.

The fact that it has outlasted everything — including ice ages and dinosaurs — should tip us off to the fact that algae has an important role to play in our destiny. It is the most vital, "ancestral" food on earth.

It just needs to be better understood.

NASA actually endorses algae as the most nutrient-dense food in the world and even wants to grow it in space! The United Nations says algae is the answer to world hunger, and in 1974 they held a global conference on spirulina.

Cultivated algae like spirulina and chlorella are known around the world as the most natural, safe, pure, eco-friendly, alkaline food crop in the world.

Yes, algae is a food crop, not a supplement.

Even the White House acknowledges algae as a food crop and included the very first "Algae Agricultural Act" as part of the 2019 Farm Bill (to encourage US farmers to grow algae here).

Algae has been used in Asia for over 50 years and is revered for its health, wellness, and beauty benefits.

Let's face it: our world is toxic, our oceans are polluted, our soil is lifeless, our children are nutrient-deprived, our bodies are fueled with sugar and our rates of cancer, heart disease, and diabetes are skyrocketing.

Something needs to change and I believe algae is part of the solution.

Algae is the most scientifically studied food in the world and its extraordinary health benefits are documented in almost 100,000 studies, many of which can be found in the National Institute of Health's online library.

The only problem with algae is that its health benefits are known by scientists but not mainstream consumers. I am the first person I am aware of to dig into all the science about algae to make it easier for you to understand.

At my company, we even dry our algae into tiny tablets that you can swallow or chew. This lets you quickly, easily, and safely get your green needs met without cooking or cleaning.

Just swallow and go.

I never planned to become an expert on algae but it seems this is where I have ended up. I didn't pick algae. It seems to have picked me, and I'm honored that it did.

I pinch myself every day because I love what I do and I love helping others improve their health with plant-based nutrition like algae.

As you look at my 10-year journey, it may appear that each step I took was carefully planned and orchestrated. I assure you it wasn't. I honestly had no idea what I was doing but just kept going.

That's what passion and purpose will do for you. You become unshakable and unstoppable.

But it hasn't been easy. I have had to learn to trust the process, not fear it. Each time I hit a roadblock, instead of panicking, I would calmly study the problem until I was guided to a solution.

This seems to be how the universe works. It requires you to do the work and take baby steps only when it feels right. Don't push and don't struggle. If something doesn't feel right, simply hit pause.

Be patient, trust your gut, and push through ego and fear.

When you do, clarity and calm will appear.

I promise.

Ten years ago, my healing food journey began with my desire to help my younger sister. My love for her led me to discover plant-based nutrition and, ultimately, algae, the most alkaline, healing, nutrient-dense food in the world.

With our food and environment so toxic and our health suffering, why wouldn't you subtract the bad and add in all the good you possibly can?

May your healing food journey be equally as powerful as mine has turned out to be.

Wishing you much health, happiness, and thanks for loving your body to bits.

Catharine Arnston MBA, is the founder and CEO of ENERGYbits®.

Catharine left her 30-year corporate career to found ENERGYbits® after discovering algae was the most nutrient-dense food in the world with healing properties unknown outside of Asia. Catharine's mission is to heal the world with mother nature's oldest food — algae.

Follow her work at EnergyBits.com.

Food Heals Podcast **Episode 276**

CHAPTER 26 – EVITA RAMPARTE: FEMALE INTELLIGENCE –– FROM CANCER TO BLISS

Female Intelligence — From Cancer to Bliss

By: Evita Ramparte

Filed Under:
#foodheals #nutritionheals #juiceheals

"You have 16 gallbladder stones. So, you will do a cleanse. You will be fasting on juices and you won't stop until they all come out... Your pancreas is weak. You have a pre-diabetic condition... Hypoglycemia...."

She said all this, just scanning my body with her eyes like a sonar-vision-equipped dolphin.

"And you have something serious going on with your reproductive organs. You need to go to a doctor and get tested."

I was thinking she was nuts.

She spoke about coffee enemas, detoxing, and fasting.

I could never fast, I thought. I loved food too much. It was the only thing that gave me pleasure back then. I was miserable.

Unhappily married to a man who was an eternal *Star Wars* fan and comic book collector, every morning we woke up to the sound of *Star Wars* music. We saw *Star Wars* 66 times during my married life. That should give you the first clue.

My professional life was just as boring. I was a legal interpreter, secretly dreaming of a career as a journalist.

And, as you can fathom, my sex life wasn't any better. I felt unfulfilled in every sense of the word.

I remember there was a moment when I was so depressed, so sad, and so overwhelmed that I more or less decided it's better to *check out* than to live so unfulfilled.

FOOD HEALS

Every cancer patient has a moment like that.

Cancer is caused first and foremost by an emotional trauma under which the brain sends a signal to shut down the immune system and blows the whistle: "Let's get out! Death is better than this kind of life."

From that moment on, the human body cannot defend itself from multiplying cancer cells. And what I ate was a highly contributing factor too.

I was literally killing myself with food.

I was addicted to fast food, meat, soda, and ice cream.

In post-communist Poland, fast food became a symbol of freedom as soon as the borders opened. We could travel outside, and junk started to flow in. Nobody warned us about the addiction and diseases it would bring.

The faces of once beautiful Polish women are now pimpled, and men morphed into tubby Kung Fu Pandas.

So, I had no intention whatsoever to jump onto some fasting regime when it was advised to me. I loved food.

Food was the one source of pleasure in my life, and I was on a 'dopamine high' looking forward to the next bite of pizza, handful of french fries, or sip of soda.

I drank 1.5 liters of soda a day, ate meat at every meal, and my cravings swung from extreme yin to extreme yang, from salty and sweet, up and down like when you press the pedals on a bike.

My body didn't lie. I was in pain.

I was carrying over 80 pounds more than I weigh today. If someone told me to carry that much baggage everywhere with me now, I would never accept that. However, back then I walked around like an 'inflammation billboard.'

I had migraines once a week and strong abdominal pain all the time.

Finally, I went to a doctor and got tested.

EVITA RAMPARTE

The gynecologist shouted aloud when she ran an ultrasound and saw the tumors on my ovaries. She said I could have cancer and needed to return for tests.

My *Star Wars* husband didn't think it was serious and ignored me saying, "You'll be fine. You'll be ok."

I knew that unless I turned into Princess Leia 2.0 he wasn't going to pay attention. I knew I wasn't going to get flowers if I ended up in hospital. And I realized he wouldn't all of the sudden love me more because I was sick.

Paradoxically, that's exactly what woke me up. I decided to do the cleanse that she told me about.

I decided to fast, detox, and see what happened next.

Who was 'she'?

She was a chiropractor by profession and native Ukrainian healer with an obvious gift of intuitive diagnosis. About everything she said, as she scanned my body that day, she was spot on, 100% accurate. And she knew it without the fancy medical equipment or a degree.

So, I decided to give it a chance.

What did I have to lose?

My ovaries. My fertility. My child yet unborn (in the future that would never happen if I didn't bow down to Nature to heal me).

My divine feminine intelligence, intuition, and instincts. My beauty that I would never see in the mirror, if I never dared to look and to love myself.

They ran the cancer tests and, on the way back from the clinic, I went shopping.

I bought an enema bag in the pharmacy, coffee in the grocery store, and a whole bunch of produce at the farmer's market.

"It's gonna be so gross," I thought to myself.

FOOD HEALS

Back then, I didn't even touch salad. My taste buds were so clogged up that nothing less than explicitly processed and super spicy was ever appealing.

The next morning, I found myself lying down on my bathroom floor, performing a coffee enema, and praying that my *Star Wars* husband wouldn't walk in the door. I was full of doubts.

"Seriously? Is this what it takes?!"

Starbucks had just entered Poland and everyone was celebrating — the oral way! But instead of drinking sugary coffee drinks, I fasted on juices as she advised. I passed gallbladders stones, colon stones, and I counted them to make sure I was done.

Sewage came out of my body with shudders, flushes of hot and cold, diarrhea, and vomiting all at the same time. It was nothing short of a drug addiction detox.

I lost seven pounds in just three days.

My senses cleared. I could smell better, see better, and actually hear the sounds around me.

Beyond a doubt, I felt like my body was healing itself like a wild animal.

I decided to continue on this path.

I returned to get the test results and doctors with sad faces wanted to send me to the Oncology hospital. They were determined like Jehovah's Witnesses, while I was like a Hare Krishna devotee trying to convert them on my newly-found lifestyle.

Obviously, we were in different pages.

I asked if they knew the cause of my disease. They laughed and said they would have a Nobel Prize if they knew the cause of cancer. I thought to myself: toxic food and toxic emotions.

So, I decided to quit both.

I knew it took me years to create this condition I was in, so while they were pressing on the accelerator, I stepped on the brakes to give myself the time to heal through cleansing and eating healthy.

EVITA RAMPARTE

I had no knowledge of nutrition back then, I had no access to American books, and no health guru had ever crossed my path. Thank God. All I had was common sense and a badass, rebellious Polish attitude that now questioned all authority.

I questioned everything I put into my mouth, way beyond just reading labels. I was being scientific. If my body is a primate — a sophisticated ape — I should look at what primates eat.

Most people eat like vultures and hyenas, hoping to scavenge life force from dead animal flesh. Some people eat like squirrels, loving nuts. Others try to eat like rabbits or cows grazing grass or chewing kale.

What appealed to me most was fruit. Fruit was calling out to me every time I visited the farmers markets, seducing me with its color, texture, and fragrance. I was salivating at fruit and salivation became my salvation.

I binged on fruit as much as I wanted and tried to overeat it.

Doctors tell you not to eat fruit because fruit has sugar, but I binged on fruit like an ape.

My jungle diet consisted of sweet, juicy, and seductive peaches, plums, apples, pears, oranges, bananas, tangerines, watermelons, grapes, and berries as well as savory tomatoes, cucumbers, zucchinis, and bell peppers.

I also ate a huge amount of gentle leafy greens with butternut squash salad being my favorite, topped with lemon juice for a salad dressing.

The entire time, instinctively, I avoided eating fat since fat blocks oxygen supply in the body and goes rancid making blood acidic. All fat does this. Fruit, on the contrary, worked like a brush than cleansed me out on the go, providing hydration, minerals, and fiber.

Four months later, I was cancer-free and I divorced my *Star Wars* husband.

Six months later, I was professionally photographed as a model for the first time.

Nine months later, I became a TV news reporter and a journalist.

One year later, I discovered Tantra and ancient erotic arts.

Nine years later, I became a mom and gave birth to a healthy baby boy.

Twelve years later, I modeled for bikini brands in Hawaii.

Today, I live my life guiding exclusive rejuvenation retreats, channeling investments into wellness ventures, and helping men and women to get healthy and become the best lovers they can be.

Sounds like fun, doesn't it?

You wouldn't guess my age today. The body never lies.

Evita Ramparte is a Love Mystic, Health Guru, and Force for Transformation. She is the author of the Amazon bestselling book *The Bliss of Cancer*.

Follow her journey at EvitaRamparte.com.

Food Heals Podcast **Episodes 57, 171, 257 & 279**

CHAPTER 27 – SAHARA ROSE: AN AYURVEDIC AWAKENING

An Ayurvedic Awakening

By: Sahara Rose

Filed Under:
#foodheals #nutritionheals #alternativemedicineheals

Flashback to 2012: I'm sitting in the humble waiting room of an Ayurvedic doctor waiting to be seen.

Pictures of Hindu deities adorn the wall: Durga riding a tiger, Saraswati sitting atop a lotus, and Dhanvantari, the four-armed god of Ayurveda, gazing back at me.

I don't have cell phone service, so my eyes drift to a poster of a meditating woman with colorful circles stacking up the centerline of her body along the muladhara chakra, svadhisthana chakra, and manipura chakra.

This office is a far cry from the hyper-sanitary, cut-and-dried doctors' offices in Boston where I spent a huge part of the past year trying to figure out what was wrong with me, but, at this point, I am willing to try anything to unravel the mysteries of my health.

I'm given a client intake form and start filling out the questions: "How is your digestion? How is your sleep?"

The questions are off to a predictable start, but they soon become a bit more personal.

"What sort of dreams do you have? Are you floating, fleeing, or flying? Are they realistic and problem-solving? Are they romantic and sweet?"

I wasn't sure why I was being asked about my dreams in a digestion consultation but, hey, it's India. You never know what you'll be asked, so just go with the flow.

A jubilant woman in a red sari approaches me with a welcoming Namaste and a deep bow.

"My name is Dr. Priyanka Gupta, I'll be seeing you today. Please follow me."

I follow Dr. Gupta through the office, and the pungent scent of oils and herbs dance in the air. She reviews my health and personality assessment, and to my surprise, just about begins telling me my life story.

"Oh, a lot of Vata I see! You must have trouble sleeping. Staying up at night thinking. You think too much."

Okay, maybe she noticed the bags under my eyes.

"Your joints always cracking. Crack, crack, crack. You're too young to have back pain."

Can she see that my posture is off? I sit up straighter.

She proceeds to look at my tongue and take my pulse.

"Very low agni," she tells me, which I later learned means "digestive fire."

"Agni very low. Not digesting food properly. Body not taking in the nutrients. Though you are eating, body is malnourished."

Malnourished? I am literally eating all day, I think, envisioning the suitcase of snacks I brought with me on my three-month volunteer trip to India.

"Agni so low that body shutting down. No more period. Very, very bad. You are too young for this."

Okay, I told her all about my digestion and dreams, but how does she know about my period?

It was true. My period had been MIA for over a year now. At first I didn't pay too much attention to my period's absence — what girl wants her period anyway? But after a year without it, I intuitively knew something was wrong, despite numerous Western doctors telling me to stop worrying and just get back on the pill.

"No period, very serious. You have all Vata (air energy) imbalances: cold body temperature, dry skin, bloating, gas, constipation, no period, weak muscles, cracking joints, insomnia, anxiety, worrying too much. If you continue like this, later in life you can get osteoporosis, Alzheimer's, and worst of all, no baby. You too pretty to not have baby."

Wait, wait, wait, hold up. Did I just hear the words osteoporosis, Alzheimer's, and infertility?

This can't be possible.

I'm a Holistic Health Coach and pretty much a raw vegan. My life is *dedicated* to health. I have my own raw-vegan nutrition blog called Eat Feel Fresh and eat all the kale in the world.

There is no way this can be accurate.

"There has to be a misunderstanding," I tell the doctor, "I eat a really healthy diet — big leafy green salads, green smoothies with spirulina, acai bowls, flax crackers…"

I continue listing off the things I normally eat on a daily basis in the US.

"Acha, this is why you have so much Vata. No more cold, raw, dry foods. Only cooked foods. Mung dhal (mung beans) and white basmati rice with lots of ghee."

"Yeah, see the thing is I'm mostly raw-vegan so I can't eat any of those foods. Can I just take some herbs instead?"

"No, Beta," calling me daughter in Hindi, "This is Ayurveda way."

"Well, this isn't going to work out," I think as I leave the office, with a list of dos and don'ts in my hand.

I figure that if I were to ever follow an Ayurvedic diet, I'd gain 50 pounds along the way and backslide to my overweight years as a young teenager when eating Taco Bell and pizza was the norm. I had spent the past few years trying to lose weight and wasn't going to risk gaining it back.

Creating an Alkaline Version

Ayurveda, by the way, is the world's oldest health system and sister science of yoga, originating in India 5,000 years ago. It's been called the age-old secret to longevity, digestive health, mental clarity, beauty and balance.

I loved the wisdom of the Ayurvedic diet for its intuitive and customizable nature, but I longed to create a way for it to be more alkaline, plant-based, and low-glycemic.

During my studies and apprenticeships, I continuously developed ways to adapt recipes for the modern alkaline kitchen.

So, I used my Vata imaginative energy and got creative, crafting recipes following Ayurvedic guidelines with a refreshing plant-based approach.

• Instead of wheat-based bread, I'd use vitamin-rich almond flour.
• In place of rice, I'd use protein-packed quinoa.
• Instead of ghee, I'd use nourishing plant-based sesame oil.
• As a substitute to cane sugar, I'd flavor with sugar-free pure monk fruit sweetener.
• In lieu of dairy milk, I'd pour hormone-balancing flax milk.
• Instead of heavy cream, I'd use skin-loving coconut cream.
• Rather than cheese, I'd use nutritional yeast or make my own nut-based versions.
• Instead of heavily cooking my food, I'd lightly sauté it to preserve its nutritional benefits.

Little did I know, I was creating the foundation for what would later become my book *Eat Feel Fresh: A Contemporary Plant-Based Ayurvedic Cookbook.*

Shortly after adapting these changes in my diet, I felt better — not just in my body but also in my mind. My digestion, menstruation, and sleep became regular, harmonized with the sun and moon.

The constant state of restlessness I carried — needing to always be doing something and going somewhere — was replaced by a deep sense of inner-peace and acceptance similar to the tranquility one feels at the end of a yoga class.

I realized that Ayurveda is so much more than a way to heal the body, but it actually shifts the very foundation of your being.

Gastronome Brillat-Savarin once said, "Tell me what you eat and I'll tell you what you are."

FOOD HEALS

But I say, "Tell me how you digest and I'll tell you who you are."

Learning about Ayurveda was like relearning a language my soul had spoken for a thousand lifetimes. The theories intuitively made sense to me instantly.

And oddly enough, whenever I had a question while writing my books, I turned internally and realized that somehow I already knew the answer.

I truly believe this isn't my first life teaching Ayurveda, and part of my dharma, or life purpose, is to modernize this ancient healing science so it can become accessible to more people, the way it's sister science yoga has over the past decade.

Ayurveda is not a diet, but rather a system that offers a deeper introspection on food and life.

Ayurveda is a living science, one that has been adapted across the centuries to fit the needs of the people it serves. It has gone from being the leading medical system in India to an underground kitchen science during British rule, and only now is it beginning to resurface.

This flexibility is what has made Ayurveda the world's oldest health system still practiced today.

I believe the time has come for Ayurveda to spread its wings and open its doors so people across the world can benefit from its age-old wisdom (without having to move to India, though that is recommended).

The holistic view of Ayurveda is more vital now than ever before. So many people, like myself, have grown tired of jumping from diet to diet, looking for the answer to health when it already exists inside of us.

All it takes is tuning in and listening.

Ayurveda provides us with the language to explain what our bodies already know.

As you read this book, you too may experience a remembrance of wisdom passed down through your ancestral lineage, no matter where in the world your roots are from.

The tenants of Ayurveda are echoed across the globe: the solution to health is to live in harmony with our nature. We are ready for a return to a system of eating that encompasses and nourishes our bodies, minds, and spirits, all of which are interconnected in ways we never could have imagined.

Sahara Rose is the bestselling author of *Eat Feel Fresh: A Contemporary Plant-Based Ayurvedic Cookbook* and *Idiots Guide to Ayurveda*, as well as host of the *Highest Self Podcast*.

Discover your mind-body type with her quiz at IAmSaharaRose.com.

***Food Heals Podcast* Episode 241**

CHAPTER 28 – LESLIE DURSO: UNAPOLOGETICALLY FURTHERING THE PLANT-BASED MOVEMENT

Unapologetically Furthering the Plant-Based Movement

By: Leslie Durso

Filed Under:
#thejourneyheals #nutritionheals #foodheals

My father told me at a young age, "Do what you love, and money will come."

This statement stuck with me as I grew up searching for those passions, searching for who I wanted to be in the world. As a super curious, free-spirited child, I knew I was never going to be built for a 9 to 5 life but also never expected to land where I am today.

I'm not sure when, but around seven or so, I started to feel a deep connection to animals. I realized we weren't that different, the cows, chickens, pigs, and me. They deserved the same respect I did, and it just didn't make sense to eat them anymore.

I never had a taste for meat anyway, so at eight years old, I firmly committed to never eating animals again.

Crazy, right?

The decision shocked my huge Italian-American, meat-loving family.

Italians speak the language of love through food, so saying 'no' to something on my plate was not exactly normal.

I remember being confused by who I was, not sure how to identify as a 'non-meat eater' around a dinner table of equally confused family members. And then, one day at school, a kid used the word 'vegetarian' to describe everything I was doing.

There was spark. I had a label. I knew what I was.

I was so excited, I ran home screaming, "I'm a vegetarian!"

FOOD HEALS

My family said, with love and laughter, "No, you're not," because they didn't think it would stick. I was only eight!

Nobody knew how serious I was.

Those first few weeks, I ate a lot of pasta, and PB & J sandwiches, but eventually I got in the kitchen and started making alternative versions of what my family ate.

Surprisingly, it wasn't hard at all.

Spaghetti, one of the most-loved staple Italian foods, is vegan already, but nobody ever mentions that. Spaghetti is comfort. Food is comfort. And if we eat the right comfort, it changes our lives.

When I was older, I moved to Los Angeles to be an actress. And I was one.

To some, you could say I was living the dream. But while I was working on a soap opera, which wasn't as glamorous as people might think, the feeling started to sink in that I wanted something more from my life.

Soap acting was limiting. It wasn't why I got into acting — I wanted to be Lisa Kudrow, the funny woman. I wanted to be a comedian, to have fun. I wanted to make people laugh. Live.

But, that wasn't how my path would unfold.

After the soap, I got a gig as "Leslie the Lab Girl" on *Bill Nye the Science Guy*. It was a blast! I wore big, dorky goggles and a white lab coat and did crazy experiments with Bill.

Creatively, it was so much different than my other work. It was fulfilling. And while I was there, mixing colored liquids in the lab, I was hit with another spark.

I wanted to teach people about food.

I had a passion for education, and the actress-vegan-Italian-American-Leslie never would have guessed what would come next. Suddenly, I knew that I wanted to bring the message of healthy living to the world.

LESLIE DURSO

But suddenly, I hit rock bottom.

Bill Nye went off the air, my marriage fell apart, and I realized this was my opportunity to start over.

I had to ask myself, "Who am I? Who do I want to be? What do I want my life to look like?"

I wanted to cook for people, I wanted to help people, and I wanted to travel the world.

Change is terrifying, but I gave myself the power to become the person I wanted to be.

Luckily, it doesn't actually take long to change your life.

The day after I decided who I wanted to be, my life was better. I came to believe that collectively we should wake up every morning thrilled and excited about who we are and what we are doing. And so that's what I created for myself.

And now, that is what I do — every single day.

Since I made the decision to change everything, I have lived my life unapologetically. This has led to appearances on *The Doctors*, *Food Network*, *Discovery Channel*, *Hallmark Channel,* and more.

I host the show *Accidentally Vegan* on FABFITFUNTV. I'm a founding Next Generation Board Member of the Humane Society of the United States. I create the vegan menus at beautiful destinations like The Four Seasons, Punta Mita.

Life is a dream and my dad was right! When you follow your passion and are true to yourself, everything falls into place.

I paved my way as a vegan chef when vegan chefs were not trendy. It wasn't always easy. It still isn't. But, I got in the kitchen and practiced. And that's where my wonderful, crazy-big family comes in — they are and always will be my best taste testers.

It's important to see the support we have around us to help live our lives as our true selves.

I am a vegan chef, and a vegan diet is what works for me. I don't put my beliefs on a pedestal because we live in a modern world full of choices. Every person on earth has different DNA, different morals, and different cultures.

Not everyone has to be vegan or gluten free or sugar free or keto. The body has evolved over thousands of years, so the key to health is listening to it. It's wise and is always talking to us.

The key is to listen and create a diet that works for you to operate at your optimum level.

I believe that eating plant-based can save the world. Certainly adding more vegetables to your plate makes you a healthier person, and it can reduce your risk of disease and even reverse many chronic and debilitating conditions.

Ann Wigmore said, "The food you eat can be either the safest and most powerful form of medicine or the slowest form of poison."

I choose medicine over poison!

Plus, the more plants you eat, the fewer animals suffer and die unnecessarily. In fact, each day you eat a vegan diet you save one animal.

And if that's not enough, the fewer animal products we all consume, the sooner we can stop global warming, save the environment, and keep mother earth alive and thriving.

The best advice I can give is to eat a large variety of plant-based nutrients.

What can heal this nation, and humanity, is moderation.

But it isn't easy. We live in a society of stuff. Status is so important, but to be the people we want to be, to be our authentic selves, we must make choices.

For example, I used to not like my legs. And a good friend told me, "They will never look as good as they do today." This is because I will age, and they will wrinkle and sag.

I will never have this moment again.

So now, I take advantage of today instead of waiting for tomorrow.

LESLIE DURSO

Life is about looking in the mirror every day and telling yourself, "I am happy," and then doing things that make you happy.

Every day we make a choice, to evolve or stay the same.

When we stop evolving, we start dying.

I choose to spend my days dedicated to what makes me happy. And that's food. Healing. Education. Animal activism. My rescue dog, Pepe.

When we know better, whatever it is — what to eat, what causes to support, who we want to be in the world — we can either stay the same or we can do better.

What harm can come from doing better?

No one ever came to me and said, "It's okay to not eat meat." As a kid, that would have made a pretty big difference in my life. But, we're told to fit into these boxes and believe that the world is as other people make it.

But that's not reality.

My story continues to evolve and unfold, teaching me every single day that the road of life may not always be a smooth one, but the key is to not let the bumps along the way change your path, but rather to inform it.

My mission is clear: to inspire beneficial, life-long eating habits for everyone. Because food truly does heal!

A vegan chef and wellness expert, Leslie Durso is the glowing face of a fresher plant-based movement that refuses to compromise style for sustainability. Walking the plant-based talk since age eight, this Southern California native has always been well ahead of the times with her meatless mindset.

She works as a consulting chef for hotels, resorts, and restaurants around the world and is currently the vegan chef at the Four Seasons, Punta Mita, Mexico.

Follow her work at LeslieDurso.com.

Food Heals Podcast Episodes 95, 96, 183, 199, 200, 201, 208, 211, 213, 219, 229, 232, 234, 237, 251, 268 & 275

CHAPTER 29 – ANGELA DEBORD HENRIKSEN MD: BECOME WHO YOU WERE MEANT TO BE

Become Who You Were Meant to Be

By: Angela DeBord Henriksen MD

Filed Under:
#foodheals #loveheals #alternativemedicineheals

I spent the first few years of my medical practice pretending that I was following the core of the Hippocratic Oath: "Do No Harm."

After eight years of diligent studying, racking up mountains of debt, sacrificing everything else, and growing in deep pride, I felt empowered in my ability to help and actually "fix" patients. Armed with an arsenal of pharmaceutical medications, I was ready to conquer any ailment that presented itself.

I did not know how incorrect and misguided I was.

I maintained the super-doctor facade until Susan walked into my office one day. Susan was an intelligent, kind, almost regal woman who I had been seeing for several years with the devastating diagnosis of Lupus.

Lupus (SLE) is an autoimmune disease in which the body's immune system essentially attacks itself.

It can destroy joints, organs, and connective tissue when infection-fighting cells see its own tissues as foreign. Susan's disease was under reasonable control because of an incredibly long list of expensive medications including narcotics, immunosuppressants, and a multitude of preventive prescriptions.

Her life was dominated by her disease, yet she smiled and asked me how my family was as she entered the tiny exam room that day. This visit had a different feel than her usual short appointments where we reviewed labs, medications, and symptoms.

She entered the room and I immediately sensed something was wrong. Something was terribly wrong. It was about to "get real," and I instinctively knew it.

187

Susan sat down and and tears welled up in her eyes. This was unlike her. She was a well-respected veterinarian in our community and was always professional, well-tailored, and collected.

She looked at me with intensity and utter hopelessness.

Slowly, Susan explained to me that she was considering ending her own life. She was about to give up her practice that she loved because her pain was so intense that she needed narcotics to get through the day.

She was not able to attend her children's sporting events because the sun on her skin would cause rashes and debilitating joint pain.

She was no longer able to be intimate with her husband. And even if she could, she did not have the energy to stay awake at the end of the long, painful days.

Her life was dominated by disease.

Susan was a very spiritual person and she simply couldn't understand how she could care for her family and continue on this Earth feeling the way she felt.

At this point, I was sobbing because I could only partially understand her misery and literally had no medicine to give her that would change or improve this daunting existence she had come to know so well.

How could I not have an answer?

Although I had no idea or plan, I vowed to help her any way I could. I gave her my home and cell numbers and pleaded with her to hold on to her life for just a little longer. This couldn't be her destiny. It wasn't fair.

We wept together, and she promised that she would hold out if even for just a few more days.

The series of events that followed were so bizarre that I can't even find the words.

First, I recalled a mentor and professor from medical school. He was a cerebral man with some eccentric ideas that matched his wild hair, which always reminded me of those pictures of Einstein. His speciality was Dermatology and Immunology, and he had always been an outside-the-box thinker.

When I called him, he told me that he was leaving for a mission trip the following day, so he could only see Susan — as a favor to me — if I could have her at his office in the next hour.

I called Susan immediately. Luckily, she just happened to have taken the day off work, gotten a babysitter for her four beautiful children, and was about 10 minutes from his office having lunch with a friend.

She hurried over.

"Susan," he said, "I don't think you have Lupus. I think you have an allergy to something you are putting in or on your body."

Unfortunately, he was leaving and couldn't do much to test or help her, but he asked her to keep a diary of every symptom she had, every food she ingested, and every product she put on her skin.

This was the one trickle of hope she needed to keep her head above water. Susan dove in and started her analysis, meticulously recording everything and analyzing it carefully.

What did we all discover? Susan was allergic to Red Dye #40!

It took a few months to figure this out, but she was diligent. The final clue came when she ate food that had red dye in it, went into the sun, and saw that she developed rashes and debilitating joint pain.

Unfortunately, this chemical was in her skin products, medications, and even the Tylenol capsules she took for headaches (in the form of the red lettering on the pills).

Determined to change her fate, Susan went on a clean-eating diet. She eliminated all processed foods completely. After just four weeks, she was a new person.

Today, Susan works full-time and takes absolutely zero medication. Her Lupus blood tests are all normal, and she continues to eat clean 100% of the time. She recently returned from a two-week vacation in Hawaii with her family and was in the sun the entire time — no symptoms!

Not only did Susan's life change for the better, so did mine. I am so incredibly grateful for the ways this woman changed my life and the epiphany that ensued. I no longer look at a patient as a disease to cure or a problem to fix.

Disease is literally dis-ease in the body. It is a sign that something is out of order, things are out of balance, and our intelligent bodies are trying to tell us that something needs to change.

Hippocrates is said to be the "Father of Medicine." He was the first to argue that disease was not a punishment from supernatural powers or Gods but rather the product of diet and living habits.

"Let food be thy medicine and medicine be thy food," was one of his famous quotes. And how true I have found that to be!

Today, I feel like I am able to give patients the ability to empower themselves over disease. I emphasize how important diet and lifestyle is to our health, while encouraging them to listen to the incredibly intelligent warning signals the body provides us.

I do this, holding an image of Susan in my mind. She is sitting at a soccer game, watching her son score a goal for the first time without pain, feeling like she has a purpose once again, and — more importantly — wanting to live.

Angela DeBord Henriksen MD, a board certified Internal Medicine physician in Indiana, is committed to helping empower people to overcome disease and better their lives through nutrition and lifestyle.

Learn more about her journey at AngelaMD.com.

Food Heals Podcast **Episode 75**

CHAPTER 30 – MELANIE BERTAUD: FOLLOW YOUR DREAMS: FROM CHRONIC DIETER TO VEGAN CHEF

Follow Your Dreams: From Chronic Dieter to Vegan Chef

By: Melanie Bertaud

Filed Under:
#foodheals #thejourneyheals #nutritionheals

It hit me pretty late. I was in my early 20s. Before then, I'd been what you might call a chronic dieter.

I couldn't have a conversation without somehow bringing it back to:
• Calories
• Weight loss or gain
• Permissible or forbidden foods
• Exactly what I'd eaten that day and whether it was okay

From around the age of 16, when I moved away from home, I hopped constantly from one diet to another.

Meal replacement diets, fat-free diets, carb-free diets, cabbage soup diets — I tried them all.

With clockwork regularity, self-disgust would throw me into the latest weightloss fad.

I would put up with nonsensical menus for a week or two, but the shakes left me feeling even hungrier than before, the snack bars sent me into a sugar-craving spiral, and processed meals never, ever filled me up.

I'd peer into the mirror, full of hope — my sacrifice *had* to be worth it. Sometimes I did lose a few pounds. Other times the scale registered no change.

But either way, each diet would end with a celebratory binge.

I'd make up for the lack of solid food, fat, or pleasure by gorging on my favorite treats.

FOOD HEALS

This cycle of dieting and feasting resulted in an unsurprisingly slow but steady weight gain. Looking back at photos, I was never as big as my head imagined, but at the time I felt like a whale.

My late teens were pretty turbulent between leaving home, rocky relationships, and dead-end jobs. Add to that an unhealthy and chaotic relationship with food, and it's not surprising my mental state suffered too.

After a break-up, something in me snapped. It was a cold, calm, and clinical feeling.

I would stop eating.

That was the answer.

Being thin was the answer.

Somehow, I had come to the core belief that if my life was crap. If I felt unhappy and kept being cheated on, it was because I was too fat to be worthy of love.

Advertisements, magazines, and the media confirmed this warped sense of reality.

What followed were several years of seriously disordered eating.

I would deny myself food all week, only to spend the weekends binging on ready-meals and frozen cheesecakes.

Or I'd go to the gym before and after work, running for hours on the treadmill to burn off the same number of calories in the two family-size bags of candy I'd eaten during the day. I actually used to think sugar was a safe food, because it didn't have any fat in it.

From vegetarian, I became vegan. I'm ashamed to say I was more motivated by having an extra excuse to refuse food rather than wanting to save animals. This was a time before veganism was hip.

I cancelled family gatherings, missed holidays, and didn't turn up to parties, either because I felt too ugly or because I wanted to avoid food.

I preferred to stay home and hide from the world.

MELANIE BERTAUD

Underneath the crazy eating patterns was darkness. I hated myself. I felt worthless and confused about what the hell I was supposed to do with my life. I had a good job in a busy office but also a vague sense that there had to be more to life.

At my core, I knew that something was missing. Something wasn't in balance. I wanted to get better so desperately.

I remember the moment clearly. It was after a particularly bad week. I'd completely lost control of my eating and take-away pizza binges had left me with a painfully bloated stomach and self-disgust so acute I couldn't bear to leave the house.

Curled up on the sofa, I had a flash of clarity — this sucked. I was only 22 with so much life still to live.

Did I really want *this* to be my future?

I had examples at work of what that might look like: women twice my age who still counted calories, spent days eating only eggs and crab sticks, moaned about their wobbly bits, and bitched about other people because they felt bad about themselves.

I may not have known what I wanted to be, but I also knew what I didn't want to be. I got up, threw out the junk food, and booked an appointment with a therapist.

I wish I could say that everything fell into place the minute I made the decision to get better.

The truth is that eating disorders and depression are both symptoms of deeper, unresolved issues and the results of what you put on your plate.

I was depressed because I felt unworthy and out of place, and weight loss had become a tool by which I made myself feel validated.

Food denial was a self-destructive mechanism I used to punish myself for not being perfect. But the food I was eating was also exacerbating my depression and anxiety and making binges more likely.

A vicious cycle, really.

FOOD HEALS

I was lucky to have a wonderful therapist who got me to address my eating patterns, and within six months, I was eating "normally." What that meant was that I was having three meals a day, plus snacks, but much of it was still non-organic, non-vegan, pre-made, and high-sugar.

So, my mood continued to be very up and down, and I still had moments when I wanted to give up and go back to my old ways.

Then I got lucky again: my little sister gave me Patrick Holford's *Optimum Nutrition Bible*. Suddenly things started to click into place. I read it ravenously like a good fiction novel — cover to cover — twice.

I couldn't believe how much of an impact food can have on the body and the mind. It was a revelation.

I also learned the impact of food on our planet, became aware of the food industry's massive carbon footprint, and realized the horror of animal farming.

That's when I began experimenting with healthy, plant-based eating and fell in love with cooking.

Life would never be the same again.

Looking back, this obsession with food, first negative and then positive, had to happen. Had I not fallen into bulimia or struggled with my mood, I wouldn't have sought out the knowledge that has brought me here.

In 2015, I quit my office job. I didn't have a clear idea of what exactly I wanted to do, but I knew I didn't want to work a pointless paper-pushing job for the next 40 years.

I wanted to — and I felt utterly ridiculous whenever I thought of this — help create a better world by helping people get healthy.

I bought a camper van and funded my travels by writing articles for wellness websites and health magazines. But it felt as though something were still missing. And that something was food.

It makes me laugh to think that I used to see food as something to fear and a tool for self-destruction.

MELANIE BERTAUD

Now, I'm a plant-based naturopathic chef, specializing in chocolate, detoxing, and mood support. I have to pinch myself sometimes to make sure I'm not dreaming.

It's not easy doing something that goes against the grain. We are told and readily accept clichés like "you have to work hard," "money is hard to come by," and "you must have a 'secure' job and a stable income."

Throughout my first few years of freelancing, I had a nagging voice at the back of my head asking whether this was enough.

"Wasn't work supposed to be a pain in the ass?"

"There are millions of writers struggling to make ends meet, millions of detox coaches without clients, and millions of chefs on low wages…how will *you* make it?"

Maybe you're facing the same kind of thing. Maybe you know you're meant to do something else but don't know where to start. Maybe you have all sorts of limiting beliefs holding you back.

All I can say is to believe in yourself. My experiences have taught me that if you believe in your abilities and act from love and compassion, you can achieve anything you set your mind to.

Don't let the past taint your present. All struggles and challenges are opportunities to learn. They are doors opening up onto endless possibilities.

I believe the first step to any positive change is what you put on your plate.

Everything you eat has a direct effect on your mood and well-being. Eat well and you'll feel well. When you feel well, you can chase your dreams.

And dreamers are what the world needs right now.

Eat well.

Be happy.

Follow your dreams.

Melanie "Mel" Bertaud is passionate about making foods that tickle your tastebuds and love you back. Her mission is to share a way of eating that's kind to your body, kind to the planet, and kind to animals.

When she's not working as a plant-based chef, detox coach, raw chocolatier, and wellness writer, you'll find her in the forest, hugging a tree or two.

Learn more at DopamineChef.com.

Food Heals Podcast Episode 142

CHAPTER 31 – AMIE VALPONE: UNRAVELING AND HEALING MY LIFE: MY PATH TO HEALTH

Unraveling and Healing My Life: My Path to Health

By: Amie Valpone

Filed Under:
#foodheals #theuniverseheals #thejourneyheals

A lot has changed from the 20-something Amie who worked at *Vogue* magazine, relying on her looks and size 0 thin body for love.

As I write this story, tears are rolling down my face.

I can't explain in words how much my life has shifted in the last decade, but I have this knowing — this strong awareness — that I went through a decade of hell so that I can now help others heal themselves when no one else can.

In 2007, just out of college, I found myself in a corporate job when my body started to shut down.

You name it, I had it.

Hundreds upon hundreds of doctors, I saw them all.

Tests upon tests, I did everything.

The Mayo Clinic, two bone marrow biopsies, muscle biopsies, Lyme disease, PCOS, Candida, SIBO, Leaky Gut, C-diff Colitis, Hypothyroidism, Epstein Barr, heavy metal toxicity, mold toxicity — the list goes on and on and on.

I was put on painkillers, steroids, and water pills at the age of 22. That was all doctors could do for me, I was told.

I felt lost, I felt confused, and, most of all, I felt like no one was on my team.

So, I realized that I had to figure out how to be a team of one and heal my own life.

AMIE VALPONE

Just as I started to research how to heal, I got so sick that I had to go on disability from my job and was given 24 *hours* to live with a diagnosis of C-diff colitis.

I laid there looking at the bag of morphine dripping into my arm with a terrible dagger-pain in my colon and I promised myself that if I survived, I'd dedicate the rest of my life to inspiring others who were struggling with their health to never give up and to stay positive.

And so I did just that.

I survived and I quit my corporate job, launched AmieValpone.com, started speaking nationwide, wrote a bestselling book, and started 'doing me' for the first time in my life.

But my own journey was not over.

In 2014, when I thought my health was totally under control, I found myself at the ripe age of 31 on the bathroom floor unable to move. I felt even more scared and lost than I had years before.

I'll never forget the moment — I can still picture it like it was yesterday — lying on the floor and about to get into an Epsom salt bath for some pain relief when I felt my mouth open and the words "I surrender" came out.

It felt like something that wasn't me was talking, and I don't know how to put words to it.

But now that I look back, I was ready. It was time. My body knew exactly what it was doing.

From that moment on, my life has never been the same and it's filled with a daily spark of magic that has guided me to exactly who and what I needed in order to end up as a healthy woman today.

My darkest moments of hopelessness, shame, pain, and anger showed me how to transform those negative emotions into trusting myself, tapping into my own creativity, and loving myself.

I've learned how to let myself be who I was always meant to be, appreciating what I have, learning to let go of what and who no longer serves me, and practicing patience with myself.

FOOD HEALS

Healing also helped me appreciate my alone time. I have learned how to nurture and care for myself with organic food, sleeping at least eight hours a night, going for walks in nature, meditating, reading mind-body books, and 'being' instead of always 'doing.'

This was not easy for me as a Type-A person but it was something I knew I had to do, even though I resisted it for years. What we resist is often what we need the most, isn't that funny? We can't even see what we need at the time of our breakdown.

This is how I found my place in the world and the work I feel I am compelled to share.

Unraveling the layers of my life while trying to better understand myself, my path, and my relationships has been such a beautiful experience. In sharing my journey of self-discovery and self-healing, I have revealed how pain reshaped my life and led me to reconnect with my true self, make peace with my past, and learn how to appreciate my body instead of fixating on the number on the scale.

Looking back, I remember feeling nothing at all for about 12 years. It was just numbness physically and emotionally. I was shut down.

Now that I am learning how to feel and how to live without being numb, it's awkward but I'm doing it. I have learned how to sit with my own pain and breathe my way through it. I unraveled the knots of my past and started to tell a new story that had my true self in it, not my shame or pain. I found myself throughout all of this and learned to love my less-than-perfect parts.

I started following my heart, trusting myself, writing more, and inspiring others. I spent countless hours trying to process my traumatic memories and started making sense of what had happened throughout the last decade.

Somewhere in all the brain fog I found the clues that helped me find my way.

Somewhere within our own healing and recovery there is a way to fill our lives with meaning. Now I know I'm here to help others heal too.

I never want anyone to go through the hell I went through for 12 very painful, traumatizing, exhausting, and expensive years trying to figure out how to be healthy in a real way. Doctors, healers, and energy workers all tried to help, but couldn't fully heal me.

I tried it all. But in the end, I learned that I had to trust and surrender. All of the answers were inside of me, just as your answers are inside of you.

It still amazes me that my unraveling and falling apart layer by layer to get to a place of self-love and self-compassion was the catalyst for something so much bigger than I could have ever imagined. It was as though there was a purpose to my health crisis. It allowed me to trust the universe and a power far greater than myself who was guiding me every step of the way.

I'm 36 as I write this, and as the years go by, I crave a deeper connection to my true self.

I'm ready to feel everything.

I'm ready to grow.

I'm ready to travel.

I'm ready for a vacation!

I'm ready to date.

I haven't done any of this in 12 years, so I feel like a kid in a candy store.

Navigating my way through pain took away all the junk in my life. I lost friends and gained soulmates, I let go of jobs and found my passion, and where I was confused, I found beautiful hints from the universe that guided me to where I was supposed to be.

When you survive a traumatic decade of your life, there's a point during your healing when you are no longer numb and all of life seems magical because just being able to get up and walk down the street is pleasurable and a huge accomplishment.

This is what I'm feeling. I often find myself on the subway wanting to yell, "I'm alive!"

The littlest moments seem like huge achievements after so many years of not being able to move or function.

Looking back, I feel bad for that 20-something, insecure girl who put all of her worth in her looks. That's no longer me.

I've realized that true self-love and healing comes from within us and our own compassion. The outside will always collapse or change at some point, so it's the inside we must focus on.

I feel more open, more alive, more whole, and more me. I feel more Amie Valpone.

I'm ready to decide what my new, healthy life looks like and I hope my story has inspired you to take back your power and live the life you're meant to live no matter what has happened in your past.

And lastly, remember that unraveling is not a bad thing, despite what anyone else says. You're not broken, you're just being guided back to your true self.

This journey is about letting go and surrendering to release the knots that hold you back, uncovering what's been hidden inside of you for too long (thinking you weren't worthy of them), releasing the labels and conditioned programming, and letting yourself be what you were always meant to be.

Let yourself unravel and you will find yourself and heal.

I guarantee it.

Amie Valpone is the author of the #1 bestselling book *Eating Clean: The 21-Day Plan to Detox, Fight Inflammation, and Reset Your Body.*

She is the founder of AmieValpone.com.

Food Heals Podcast **Episode 92**

CHAPTER 32 – TIM KAUFMAN: DO A LITTLE MORE THAN YA DID YESTERDAY

Do a Little More Than Ya Did Yesterday

By: Tim Kaufman

Filed Under:
#foodheals #exerciseheals #nutritionheals

Walking out of the doctor's office, reality finally sank in: My wife and kids would lose a husband and father within the year.

My blood pressure was 255/115, my resting heart rate was 125, and I was on enough prescriptions that I couldn't fit them in a weekly pill organizer.

My cholesterol at 300 and triglycerides at 279 were off the charts, literally.

My weight was so out of control that the doctor could no longer weigh me in his office. "You are well over 400 pounds."

I was on a ton of opioids, I was self-medicating, and I struggled with a Fentynal and alcohol addiction.

I was having trouble breathing and had severe sleep apnea.

And because I was born with a genetic disorder called Ehlers Danlos Syndrome, my joints are very loose and hyper mobile. So, the excess weight was too much for my already destroyed joints to handle.

I was constantly on crutches, canes, and immobilizers.

I was cast and fitted for very expensive leg braces that would hold my legs from buckling.

My wife was actually had to put my socks and shoes on me in the morning.

Nothing was working and my life was spiraling out of control. I was going to die and I don't know if I really cared. I would try diets and I would lose some weight and then gain it all back. It was a vicious cycle.

The more I hurt, the more I medicated — the more I medicated, the more I hurt. And, as a result, I had lost passion for life. I was just surviving, hoping I wouldn't wake up the next morning.

I was committing a sort of slow suicide.

Every day I could see the hurt in my wife's eyes as I grew more and more unhealthy. We were also in the process of dealing with both my father and her mother having been diagnosed with aggressive cancers. It was very hard to see the pain she was going through.

One night I realized that she would soon have to deal with the same pain as a result of the choices I was making. I had become an expert on excuses and reasoning why I had become who I was. In the back of my mind, I think I knew that at least some of what I was going through was self-induced.

If I even had a chance to save my wife from more pain I was going to give it a try.

Although I really didn't care about myself, I figured it was pretty selfish to put her through another death (self-induced, no less).

When you watch someone struggle to stay alive you can't help but appreciate life no matter how bad you think you have it. While I complained about how much my knees hurt, I watched my loved ones struggle to just breathe.

Perspective is an amazing thing!

I made some phone calls and started the process to get a bariatric surgery (or gastric bypass). I had done the research, and this sounded like the best option. I was scheduled for the meetings and pre-op tests because I had to get clearance from my primary doctor.

This was just a formality, or so I thought.

My wife was skeptical, which was weird because as an addict you learn to become a master at manipulation. I just couldn't sell this one to her. I thought by taking her to my doctor he would assure her of what a good decision this was.

FOOD HEALS

She and I sat down with my doctor and I told him my plan. He explained that he had approved everyone who had ever asked for the surgery. He said many people have had success with it. However, he would not sign off on the surgery for me. I was just too sick.

I was enraged, to put it mildly. I was not healthy enough and he thought that my joints would become worse if I had the surgery.

So there I was, my last hope was dashed.

I have no idea what transpired in my head that night — I am more than positive it was divine intervention — but I grabbed a notebook and wrote down the following day's date at the top. Directly underneath I wrote: "This is the first day of the rest of your life."

I got on my knees and I asked the Lord to give me enough strength to change just one small thing a day.

Underneath that I wrote: "Goal: Get up from chair 2x."

This whole process was way out of character for me. Writing things down is for old people or weirdos. Anyway, I figured if I could get up from a chair once, I could do it twice.

The next day, that's exactly what I did.

If someone saw me they would have thought I had lost it. Every day I added just one small change. Sometimes it was just to walk up four extra stairs, but it was always a little more than I did the day before.

I started to log my food but I actually had no idea what real food was. In time, my food choices started changing. I started to eat things that made me feel better instead of putting me into a food coma.

Little changes, many hours of research, and documentaries like *Forks Over Knives, Vegucated, Engine 2 Kitchen Rescue, Fat Sick and Nearly Dead,* and *The Gerson Miracle,* to name a few, gave me an entirely new perspective on food.

The more small successes that I had and better food choices that I made, the more I wanted to stay focused.

Since I started to focus on change, my life has completely flipped upside down. Every single aspect of my life has changed. I now hate going to sleep because I'm afraid I'm going to miss something.

I've had so many opportunities that sometimes I think it's all a dream.

But it's true. I've climbed mountains, hiked on the Appalachian Trail, and cycled 100-mile centuries. I have run 5ks, 10ks, a bunch of half marathons, and a couple of full marathons. I have completed a couple Ironman 70.3s and, believe it or not, I did a 50k and a 50-mile ultra-marathon on some crazy trails.

Imagine that, I am supposed to be in a wheelchair! I shed 200 pounds and my doctor now refers patients *to me* for advice. How cool is that?

The best part of this whole thing is that my wife has been there by my side every step of the way. She has done nothing but support me and she has been my rock. She too has had some major changes in her life. As a result of my lifestyle changes, hers changed by default too. She lost 90 pounds by eating plants too! We love life together and are making memory after memory.

I thank the Lord for my health and happiness every day. I am truly grateful for the second chance he's given me, and I am on a mission to not only appreciate it but to pass it on to anyone who will listen.

It's not magic; it is quite simple. Just do a little more than you did yesterday.

My wife and I are now thriving on a plant-based diet free of meat, dairy, and oil with starch, vegetables, and fruit as our main fuel source. My total cholesterol is 112 and triglycerides are 74.

I eat more now than I did when I weighed 400 pounds but I am never hungry and I never count calories. I can't wait to wake up and enjoy each day.

I was graciously blessed with a second chance and I refuse to waste it. The best part of the whole thing is that anyone can do what I did. A whole food, plant-based lifestyle is out there for anyone who wants it.

If you are even thinking about changing your diet please watch the movie *Forks Over Knives*. Read the *Starch Solution* and the *China Study, Eat to Live* is another great one! Also, check out Nutrition Facts.org.

My mission for my blog is to document as much of the information and practices that got me this far. I have a long way to go and I'm not even close to where I want to be but I'm a long way from where I started.

I don't have all the answers and I may be wrong about some things, but I will do my best to be as real as possible and to help anyone who sincerely wants it.

Please don't get freaked out about the plant-based lifestyle. If someone would have told me before 2014 that I'd be eating this way, I would have tossed my burger at them!

Give it a try, it won't cost you a dime.

Results are VERY typical *

"Eat plants and move your body. All ya gotta do is a little more than yesterday."

Tim Kaufman was a 400-pound, crippled addict who was almost immobile. He adopted a whole food, plant-based lifestyle and now thrives as an athlete enjoying life to its fullest.

You can find him at FatManRants.com.

Food Heals Podcast **Episode 137**

CHAPTER 33 – DEBI CHEW: FROM PICKETING TO PASSION

From Picketing to Passion

By: Debi Chew

Filed Under:
#foodheals #alternativemedicineheals #exerciseheals

As I walked around the perimeter of the shopping center at age 47, sign in hand for the umpteenth time, I thought to myself, "There has to be more to life than this."

We were in the fourth month of contract negotiations, and my patience was running thin. The weather had turned cold and money was getting low.

Both my husband and I worked for the same company, and four months without a paycheck was becoming an issue. We had three kids at home and a mortgage to boot.

I decided to put those worries aside and joined a few of my co-workers who were having some coffee in a small alcove of the shopping center.

The conversation was of course about the strike and how much longer it was going to drag on. One of my co-workers named Robert explained to the group how thankful he was that his wife had such a great job as a nurse at a local hospital.

My ears perked up.

I had always dreamed of becoming a nurse. I loved helping people and being a nurse was the best way to do that.

I don't know if it was my exhaustion or the fact that I just didn't care anymore but I blurted out, "I always wanted to be a nurse."

The group went silent and all eyes turned to me.

Robert shot back with, "Well, why don't you do it then?"

DEBI CHEW

Was he crazy? I was 47 years old with very little college and not much confidence. I looked at him and said, "I'm too old, I have hardly any college, how could I do it?"

He smiled and said, "Why don't you go to the local college and talk to a nursing counselor and see what it would take?"

Believe it or not, that thought had never crossed my mind.

From that moment on, all I could think about was, "Is this really possible? Could I pull it off at my age?"

I went home and told my husband what happened. He said, "Go for it. Go talk to a counselor, and I'll support you whatever you decide."

Wow, this door just went flying open and my dream was on the other side. I jumped through that door and made an appointment with a nursing counselor.

That decision would change the rest of my life.

I sat in the waiting room and hoped they'd call my name soon. I was nervous and thought about getting up and leaving. Who was I kidding anyway?

But then, the door to the office opened and a well-dressed woman with blond hair and a sweet smile called my name. As I walked into the office, she pointed to a chair across from her desk. I took a couple of deep breaths, hoping she wouldn't notice how nervous I was.

She smiled at me and asked, "What can I do for you today?"

I explained why I was there and expected her to pat me on the head and tell me, "Sorry, we don't accept people of your age to the nursing program."

Instead, she pulled out a file and explained to me the classes I would need to take to qualify. To my shock and delight it was only a few classes.

Unfortunately, the classes were actually starting today and I would have to go to a class and try to add it to get in this semester.

FOOD HEALS

I quickly looked over the list of classes and saw that I needed to take some kind of art history or music course. There was an art appreciation class starting that night. So, I ran over to the registration office, signed up for the semester, and made my way to the class.

As luck would have it, there was an opening and I was able to add it that night.

So started my journey to the nursing program. While fulfilling my prerequisites, I decided to take a phlebotomy class and apply for a position at the hospital I wanted to work in. I continued to work at the grocery store part-time too.

With the support of my three kids and husband, I was able to complete the nursing program and graduated at the age of 52. I was hired as a nurse at my hospital right after graduation.

Working in the hospital, it became apparent to me that nutrition was important and there was a real connection between your diet and a lot of disease processes. I started doing research, watching documentaries, and started changing my diet.

One of the documentaries I watched was *Forks Over Knives*. It opened my eyes, and I gradually transitioned over the next month to a vegan diet.

In August of 2013, I went for my yearly physical and there were some irregularities in my lab work. I was referred to a gastroenterologist. He diagnosed me with autoimmune hepatitis and wanted to start me on steroids right away. I refused, knowing all the side effects. I was not willing to go through that.

I was sure I could heal myself through diet.

After about three weeks of progressively getting worse, my doctor told me that if I did not start the steroids that he would put me in the hospital. Reluctantly, I went on the steroids to save my life.

I had a lot of time on my hands, bedridden for weeks, so I searched the internet for answers, for cures. I joined a support group online and so many of these people had to quit their jobs and had been on medications for years with horrible side effects.

I decided that would not be my life!

DEBI CHEW

Through a series of events, I found a doctor in New York City who specialized in autoimmune hepatitis I was able to send him all my labs and tests. I then had a phone conversation with him, I gave him my complete history, and he confirmed that I did have autoimmune hepatitis and told me that he would put together an herbal protocol for me.

He promised I would be off the steroids in about six weeks.

Figuring I had nothing to lose, I started the Chinese herbal protocol and my numbers started improving, so my regular doctor started decreasing my steroids. I hadn't told him yet about this treatment. I was afraid that he would be upset with me, so I waited, and my numbers kept declining.

After about three weeks I told him what I had been doing and I was surprised that he was not upset. He didn't really believe in it, but he figured it wasn't going to hurt me.

After about six weeks on the protocol, my numbers were very close to normal and my doctor took me off the steroids completely, saying "We will know very quickly if you are in remission because your numbers will start climbing right away."

He sent me in for lab work and I held my breath until I got the results. My numbers were normal, and they have remained normal ever since.

I was determined to stay healthy, so I cleaned up my diet to become a whole food plant-based vegan. I needed a goal, so I decided to sign up for my first half marathon. I wanted to prove to myself that I was strong and healthy. I started training and eating very clean.

I set a goal for myself to finish the half marathon in under three hours.

In October of 2013, I finished the half marathon in two hours and fifty-seven minutes. I remember around mile nine getting very emotional. The magnitude of what I was doing hit me. Just a few months prior I couldn't get out of bed I was so weak and sick, and now I was on my way to finishing my first half marathon.

I realized how strong and determined I am.

I realized that anything is possible.

I haven't slowed down yet.

Next, I wanted to help people transition to a plant-based diet on a bigger scale. So, at the age of 60 I started my YouTube channel, Chew on Vegan.

I make cooking videos and show you how easy it is to eat a plant-based diet. Age is no longer a deterrent for me. If you say you're too old or too young, that's an excuse not to try.

If you don't try, you may never find out how truly amazing you really are and what you can become.

Debi is a full-time RN and YouTube personality. On her channel *Chew on Vegan*, Debi shares quick and easy recipes for people with busy lives and families.

Follow her at YouTube.com/ChewOnVegan.

Food Heals Podcast **Episode 221**

CHAPTER 34 – KHRISTEE RICH: FROM SLEEPWALKING TO SEEING THE WORLD WITH FRESH EYES AND BRIGHT COLORS

From Sleepwalking to Seeing The World With Fresh Eyes and Bright Colors

By: Khristee Rich

Filed Under:
#foodheals #theuniverseheals #spiritheals

I stepped into the specialist's office with my stack of neatly, typed, stapled pages. Everything in the office was a muted brown, but I hoped that today was the day that I would see in color again.

I prayed that this doctor would be the one who was finally able to discover the root cause.

I had been a healthy girl all of my life, but for the last 15 years, I struggled with a debilitating, chronic illness and no one knew why.

The doctor walked in briskly with energy and confidence.

"What brings you in to see an Infectious Disease Specialist today?" he asked.

I presented him with my long, detailed notes of every test I had taken from MRIs to CAT Scans to a colonoscopy, endoscopy, and more. I detailed how my symptoms had escalated over the years. I gave him a list of all of my supplements and vitamins, my food allergies, and every alternative healing modality I tried.

Everything was contained neatly in those typed, stapled pages.

"Wow. You did all of this for me?" he asked. "This is very thorough."

"I have been sick for so long — 15 years. No one believes me. Please, can you do some further testing?"

"This is very detailed. I believe you," he said. "Something is wrong. We will get to the bottom of this. We will run more blood tests."

KHRISTEE RICH

A feeling of warmth flowed through my body. He was the first doctor who listened to my full story of how I became mysteriously sick in Europe and never recovered, how doctors quickly labeled me as depressed, then stressed, then eventually a hypochondriac when I returned repeatedly asking for further testing.

Ultimately, I was misdiagnosed with fibromyalgia, an incurable illness, and my primary care doctor said, "There is nothing more I can do to help you, so you have to accept your fate and hope to marry a rich man who will take care of you."

Wow.

Others may have given up, but I persevered. I knew it was not my fate to be sick for the rest of my life.

A week later, I returned to the new doctor's office for my blood results. I sat on the examining table, the pristine white paper under me.

The doctor entered briskly and full of energy, wearing his spotless, long, white coat.

"Khristee, I am so glad we ran further testing! I have discovered the root cause of your illness."

"Great!" I said, excitedly. "What is it?"

"You have extremely high levels of heavy metals in your blood: lead and mercury. It's off the charts! Within all the years I have been practicing, I have never seen such high levels in any of my patients. Khristee, do you realize that your levels are so high that you should have suffered paralysis or brain damage? It's a miracle you didn't."

I was stunned.

"You do not have an infectious disease. You are going to need to see another specialist — a toxicologist — and have weekly chelation therapy. With your levels, you will probably have to go for treatment for at least a year or longer in New York City. I will report you to the state of Connecticut as having been exposed to an environmental hazard. The state likes to be informed of such findings. I am sure they will contact you."

FOOD HEALS

The door clicked as he left.

Everything seemed brighter.

I felt like a kid in a candy shop. Finally, my biggest dream had come true: to discover the cause of my illness. I wanted to jump for joy!

My thoughts raced.

First, ecstatic:
"Wow, heavy metals?! He figured it out! I knew there was something wrong! I am so glad I found him! I am so happy!"

Then, to confusion:
"Wait, I have heavy metals? How did this happen?! I have been exposed to an environmental hazard?! I have the highest toxicology report ever???"

To reassurance:
"It doesn't matter; there is a treatment. I am going to be fine. I am going to be healthy again!

Finally I had hope! Finally I had a clear direction of how to improve my health. Finally someone believed me!

I drove home in joy and immediately went onto Google.

"What is chelation therapy?" I typed in to the search field.

I researched and learned that chelation therapy is one of the few substances that can pass between the blood brain barrier. Because of this, chelation therapy is very controversial.

It is the only cure or treatment that Western Medicine recommends for heavy metal toxicity but because the chemicals can pass between the blood brain barriers it may cause disastrous side effects such as paralysis, brain damage, and even death.

Finally I found a cure, but my treatment could potentially kill me. What?!

Not only that, the treatment was costly. I didn't have any health insurance at the time. How would I afford a year of treatment?

Lastly, it was very painful. I didn't tolerate pain well. Was I strong enough for the treatment?

Similar to chemotherapy, the chemicals are inserted intravenously and remove what protects the body and keeps it balanced. Chelation therapy strips the body of all vitamins and minerals.

Tennis players show us the anguish of losing potassium and magnesium on the tennis court after a long match. Imagine the extreme pain and cramping of losing all of your essential vitamins and minerals, every week.

Ouch!

I added it up in my head. After 15 years of debilitating illness, I received the correct diagnosis, there was treatment, but it was costly, painful, and might result in my death.

I shook my head. It didn't make sense.

I had had enough of this health rollercoaster. I proclaimed that I would be well in one month!

"Forget this," I said. "I am a healer. I will heal myself! I will be healthy in one month!"

I sat back down at the computer, but this time with a different intention.

I researched natural ways to chelate, attach and remove the heavy metals from my body, without side effects. Heavy metals must attach to other substances, to draw them out of the body. Heavy metals do not naturally come out of the body over time. Instead if untreated, they will accumulate in the body.

That is what happened to me. My levels were so high that my doctors thought I had been ingesting heavy metals for years. Still, it was a mystery how I got them into my bloodstream.

With the help of Google, in a matter of minutes, I found natural foods and supplements, with no side effects, that would chelate — or remove the metals — from my bloodstream. I started taking them religiously.

FOOD HEALS

Each morning, I drank a muddy, green-colored smoothie with vibrant, kelly green chlorella. The smoothie included bright white spoonfuls of coconut butter. Yum!

Also, I made a delicious, creamy, moss-colored, cilantro pesto and ate it, every day, over tri-color pasta or with bright orange carrot sticks as a dip or afternoon snack.

For the first time in my life, I meditated. I had always wanted to learn this! For 20 minutes every day, twice daily, I sat upright, breathed deeply, and cleared my mind. Golden balls of light pulsated into my body.

And for exercise each day, I walked down my cul-de-sac and back with my excited, jet-black Labrador retrievers tugging me in each direction. We were excited to smell the green grass, see the wild raspberry bushes, and feel the warm sunlight.

My daily mantra was, "Khristee, you will be healthy by the end of the month!"

Due to my high toxin levels, my doctors drew my ruby-red blood every three to four days to see if the levels continued to go up. With my new regime, my levels were not going up. Instead, they started to go down, down, down.

At the end of the month, they checked it for the last time, and my levels were zero! Not a trace.

From the highest levels my doctors had ever seen to zero in one month!

My doctors scared me into thinking that there was only one treatment and that it would take at least a full year or more of chelation therapy, but following my own intuition and becoming my own health advocate, I was able to heal myself naturally in just one month.

Finally, I had my life back!

Better yet, it was because of me!

I did it!

I healed myself!

Never take for granted the amazing healing power of good food, supplements, breathing (meditation), positive thinking, and believing in miracles.

Khristee Rich is a Healer and Spiritual Teacher. She works with empathic women who have a chronic illness, chronic pain, and who have tried everything to no avail before working with her. Her holistic healing empowers, spreads joy, and helps you to live your best life.

Follow her at TheDancingCurtain.com.

***Food Heals Podcast* Episode 135**

CHAPTER 35 – SHELBY WEBB: A BLESSING IN DISGUISE

A Blessing in Disguise

By: Shelby Webb

Filed Under:
#foodheals #gratitudeheals #theuniverseheals

My health journey started when I was diagnosed with Polycystic Ovarian Syndrome or PCOS, a hormone disorder.

This diagnosis was a scary one because not only did my gynecologist not know how I got it, she didn't know how to cure it.

I was never asked about my diet or lifestyle. I was simply told I had a hormone disorder that was probably the reason for my cluster of symptoms that included acne, lack of menstruation, hirsutism (unwanted, male-pattern hair growth in women), and weight gain.

I was given a new acronym, a prescription for birth control, and well wishes.

PCOS is a woman's worst nightmare.

Your very femininity is under attack. I went six months without a period and no one could tell me why.

The truth is: my body was toxic.

I lived in Milan, Tennessee, a small town full of farmers but no organic food in sight. Before I received the diagnosis, I didn't think much about what went into my mouth or on my skin.

I bought makeup at Walmart. I didn't read labels. I ate processed food.

You could say I lived unconsciously. I thought health was something that you had or lacked due to chance or maybe God's will.

Like many Americans, I knew a lot about disease but not much about health.

The years following my diagnosis were confusing and painful. I continued to be extremely self-conscious about my body and consulted various conventional doctors for the different issues including a dermatologist about the excess weight I was carrying in my face.

His suggestion instead of diet changes and more exercise? Liposuction.

Yes, liposuction, for a girl in her early 20s.

PCOS affects women in the most painful ways: it causes them to gain weight, have cystic acne, and not menstruate (and thus not ovulate). For some, PCOS is paired with insulin resistance.

While a cause has not been definitively proven, suspected culprits include BPA (a hormone-disrupting chemical found in plastics), excess estrogen, and other environmental factors that come with being a woman in the toxic world we live in today.

A few years later, I picked up a book called *Eat Right 4 Your Type* by Dr. Peter J. D'Adamo. This book shares the theory that our bodies digest foods differently based on our blood types. I turned to the section on my blood type, A.

The more I read, the more something inside me whispered, "This is it!"

So much of the information resonated: individuals with my blood type have high cortisol levels, are highly sensitive, have sluggish digestive systems, and thrive on plant-based diets and low-intensity exercise.

I took this knowledge and began to increase the 'highly beneficial' foods and reduce the 'avoid' foods. My body began to respond because I was finally giving it the fuel it needed!

I also quit running, which was the bane of my existence and never helped me lose weight anyhow (because it raised my cortisol levels).

I went completely pescetarian for several years, lost a considerable amount of weight (over 1/5 of my former body weight), and saw improvements in my skin and overall vitality.

The blood type diet worked for me because it gave me what I had been looking for: a lifestyle plan, not a diet. A plan is something you can incorporate a little or follow completely.

Many people use it in an 80/20 way. It's not a fad diet, it is about honoring the uniqueness of your body. You learn what food is medicine and what food is poison to your blood type. You don't have to eliminate anything completely. It never felt restrictive; it felt nourishing.

I learned that conventional medicine doesn't have the time, or frankly the interest, in helping prevent disease. Doctors don't make money when you're healthy. I know now that my health is not my doctor's responsibility; it is mine.

We have so much more power than we are led to believe.

No one else had the answers to my specific health concerns around PCOS, not my doctors and not my family.

No one was going to be able to find the answers, and that was actually the point: I was given the task by the Universe to heal myself so that I could become the type of person who perseveres and heals herself.

I became a healer by healing myself, which led me to become a Holistic Nutrition Consultant and help other people heal themselves too.

My body didn't heal when I did what everyone else was doing: running, eating tons of meat and processed foods, counting calories, or restricting food.

The blood type diet felt like giving myself a big hug. My healing came from making incremental changes, counting chemicals, refusing artificial sweeteners, being the weird girl who always brings her lunch, incorporating organics as much as possible, seeing a Naturopath, using key supplements, and reading labels.

After years of taking the birth control pill, I went off of it in my early 20s and to my surprise, my periods came back.

I had been told this was not possible without the pill, but my periods have now been regular for more than five years.

At the beginning of my health journey, I was a health evangelist. I thought if everyone could just hear my story, they would begin their own journeys right away!

Today I know that healing is personal, and we don't get to decide when others are ready. All we can do is be examples.

Healing our world is not a matter of forcing our viewpoints on others, instead it is a matter of being an example of how good it feels to be in good health.

I know now that I don't have to heal everyone I meet. I healed myself and that is enough.

I also know that being good examples of health will plant seeds for people more than we realize.

My health journey continues today, and every day I see the power of my daily habits on my long-term health.

I now also see my diagnosis as a blessing because it made me start paying attention to my health at a much younger age than most, which I believe will help me prevent diseases for the rest of my life.

My journey taught me personal responsibility. It taught me my own power.

While PCOS is not something you ever are completely free of, I now control what I can control: what I eat, what I put on my skin, my stress levels, my willingness to make changes, and trust in my Higher Power.

My PCOS journey introduced consciousness into my life, which bled into more areas than just my nutrition. In 2015, my journey in consciousness helped me get sober after years of alcohol abuse.

That's the thing about creating consciousness: you can't introduce it into one area of your life and not expect it to spill into the other areas.

I'm ready for the rest of my journey, no matter where it takes me.

PCOS gave me the ultimate challenge: "Can I love my body, even though it's not perfect?"

Only when my answer to that question was "yes" could I begin to heal.

My body healed itself because I gave it the right tools.

The sooner we stop outsourcing our health and take responsibility for it, the faster we are able to heal —body, mind, and spirit.

Food HEALS, fam!

Shelby Webb is a writer, nutrition nut, and soberista living in Saint Paul, Minnesota.

She writes on Instagram at @shelbysimmonssays.

Food Heals Podcast **Episode 35**

CHAPTER 36 – MEG AND KOMIE VORA: EMBRACING YOUR UNIQUENESS TO FIND YOUR PURPOSE

Embracing Your Uniqueness to Find Your Purpose

By: Meg and Komie Vora

Filed Under:
#theuniverseheals #thejourneyheals #braveryheals

No one ever really comes into this world knowing who they want to be or what they are going to be.

A lot of us are told though — whether by your parents or society — and the allure to conform to pressures is always present.

We sisters were born into a typical, Indian family and grew up in a nice, suburban American neighborhood.

Think of the stereotypes. That was us.

Being females, with no brothers, and the first generation born in the US came with a certain mold to adhere to. Many of the traditional expectations were in place, a big one being "never eat meat," which stemmed from our mother who was brought up Hindu and our father who was raised Jain.

Jainism is a lifestyle that follows the principles of "Ahimsa," which translates to "no-violence towards any living being." A household based on the elements of compassion were the norm.

We didn't know it then but this would serve as a foundation for our future endeavors.

Ever since we were little we always felt like something was amiss. We physically looked different than everyone around us, had a different diet, and spoke a different language. We were the only Indians and the only vegetarians at our school and in our neighborhood.

The perfect recipe for bullying.

FOOD HEALS

This meant bringing lunch from home, not buying lunch like everyone else, and often being outcast as a result. None of the kids were familiar with Indian food so they deemed it as "gross" to look at and even worse to smell.

No one wanted to sit with the brown girls who ate the strange food and had the second-hand clothes to match.

We were lonely, insecure, and so desperate to fit in that one Taco Tuesday when the cafeteria was serving up their typical taco trays, we managed to snag one.

Not understanding the process behind meat or what it consisted of, we made a taco, sprinkling the meat on top as the final step. We hoped the kids would see that we too, were one of them.

Luckily, a teacher caught on and grabbed the tray from us. All the staff knew we were strict vegetarians. She told us we couldn't eat it and made a scene about it in the lunchroom.

This was the exact opposite of what we wanted to have happen.

Now, not only did the other kids see us as weird but, according to them, we were dumb too. This continued into junior high and high school. The more we tried to mask who we were at our core, the more it seemed to just smack us in the face as a reminder.

We thought once we got older things would change and we would start feeling some form of inclusiveness, but the reality was we felt further apart than anything.

And aside from the obvious external reasons as to why we might feel out of place, something started to take shape internally.

We didn't know what it was, but it was off.

We realized our interests were also serving as a huge disconnect. At the time, we were at an uncomfortable juncture. We felt happy for everyone around us who were content with where they were — happy to stay in their comfort zones — but we couldn't get behind that for ourselves.

We wanted more and started feeling guilty that we weren't on the same page yet again.

MEG AND KOMIE VORA

It was right around this time we discovered Los Angeles: the land of opportunities, a melting pot of big dreams and even bigger personalities. Exactly what we felt our missing link was.

The people we met in LA were people who 'got us.' We were all speaking the same creative language. We all aspired for more and wanted to accomplish things that were greater than ourselves.

This was a stark contrast to what we had been exposed to back home, and we were hooked.

We knew we had to be there; we just didn't know how yet. As we continued to venture out and try to change the cards we were dealt to align with what we were seeking, the universe stepped in.

We met a woman who introduced us to the world of styling, which in turn landed us on sets of music videos. This was hilarious because at the time we didn't even know styling was a thing. We were in awe.

"This is something people do and actually get paid for it?!"

It was as if we had been given a golden ticket to Willy Wonka's chocolate factory.

We had already been "styling" all along because we made up outfits for our friends on trips and nights to go out. This was what creating "looks" entails in the fashion world. It's funny how things come full circle.

As much as we loved going to school and learning traditional subjects, we were finally able to utilize the creative sides of our personalities. It was a dream.

We were already using our wardrobe as a vehicle to express ourselves. We were made fun of for being too out of the box, dressing in a way that just didn't make sense to those around us.

They didn't understand our affinity for inserting safety pins to add a hint of toughness, slapping vintage patches on to make clothing more personal, forever cutting up shirts to make them stand out, or making tweaks to our Indian clothes too.

Now, we were getting to do this on Hollywood sets!

It was surprising. We couldn't believe something that came to us completely naturally and was never looked at as a professional thing to do was so in demand. The exact thing people back home laughed at us for was really something people in Hollywood wanted from us.

Go figure.

We started traveling back to India again during college because our parents wanted to make sure there was a good balance between our Eastern and Western worlds.

Still deconstructing and reconstructing our Indian clothes, we decided to start using leftover scraps (see we were already putting sustainability into play!) into making more American looking outfits, and we brought these back with us.

Every time we saw our pieces back in the States, it was a reminder that this creativity was such a big part of who we are.

That being said, we were still pushed into sticking to the path that our culture expected of us. This meant going to college and earning a proper degree. Upon completion, it was imperative to have a career that paid a salary, not a job that offered an hourly wage.

Even as we were entering the world of adulthood after college, we were still being told what to do. It was a strange time.

The dreams our parents had for us were not the dreams we had for ourselves. We weren't satisfied working these 9-5 positions that gave us a secure salary. And that nagging feeling of not belonging was popping up again.

We couldn't shake it.

We would come home from work and have conversations about how unhappy and unfulfilled we were feeling in our current situations. This opened up the floodgates for a new type of dialogue — how wonderful it would be to have a fashion company together instead!

However, it couldn't just be *any* clothing line, it needed to have substance and a purpose.

MEG AND KOMIE VORA

As we dug deeper, we realized that in order to be the most authentic, we needed to stay true to ourselves. We needed to figure out what drives us and how to contribute in a meaningful way to the world.

This translated as going back to what was a true constant for us — being lifelong vegetarians coupled with our ingrained desire to create. At the time, the link between animals, compassion, and cruelty was evident to us through food but not so much through fashion.

As we became more well-versed, we turned vegan and simultaneously started to build our own personal cruelty-free wardrobe. The pickings were slim.

As a lover of luxury houses and their products it was really frustrating to see the most stylish, highest quality, well-constructed items were usually made out of leather, fur, silk, or wool.

Why did luxurious have to come at the cost of other animal's life?

As we connected all of these dots, it became more apparent that Delikate Rayne, our brand, was necessary. It was the missing piece to change how luxury is perceived while educating consumers on why compassion and sustainability is important not just in fashion but in life in general.

As we continue to grow our company and face the challenges entrepreneurship brings, we have learned a lot. Looking back, we now understand that our uniqueness — the things that made us feel like outsiders — were actually our golden treasures.

If we weren't raised vegetarian on the principles of Jainism and Hinduism our parents instilled in us, we wouldn't have understood compassion so early on and wouldn't have had the basis to connect that to our hidden creative desires, which came full circle when we built Delikate Rayne.

Whatever your idea of success is, whatever path you are on, as long as it feels purposeful and fulfilling to you, it is the right one.

What might be perceived as a negative can actually be a pillar of strength.

We are all powerful and have something to offer even if you haven't discovered it yet.

The one thing we do know is that no one in the world is made up of the same combination of atoms and molecules as you, even if you are a twin or triplet. You have now found your first element of uniqueness.

So start there, embrace that.

Sometimes being the black sheep works out for the best. You never know when you may be on the cusp of a new-found purpose.

Meg and Komie Vora are sisters and co-founders of award-winning cruelty-free lux label, Delikate Rayne.

They use their company as a vehicle to redefine luxury while spreading awareness and educating consumers on the importance of a compassionate and sustainable wardrobe and lifestyle.

Learn more at: DelikateRayne.com.

Food Heals Podcast **Episode 245**

CHAPTER 37 – ELLA MAGERS, MSW: THE ROCKY ROAD TO AN EMPOWERED VEGAN LIFE

The Rocky Road to an Empowered Vegan Life

By: Ella Magers

Filed Under:
#foodheals #exerciseheals #loveheals

I was seven years old.

I got in the car, as my mom picked me up after school to take me to gymnastics practice and asked how my day was.

I told her we had learned about Daniel Boone that day (one of our first American folk heroes who carried around a shotgun and wore a racoon hat).

I was confused though.

"Daniel Boone was supposed to be a hero, but he was not, Mom," I said. "He was a mean man. He killed and ate animals."

My mom was honest with me.

She said, "Well, Ella, we are just fortunate now-a-days. We get to go to the grocery store to buy our meat."

And it was at that moment that I connected the food on my plate with the animal that it was. I was horrified!

"I'm not going to do that anymore."

And from that day on, I never ate meat again.

I was extremely fortunate to have the loving parents I did. They let me be me and gave me a lot of autonomy to explore my place in the world.

Not only did I stop eating meat, it was as though I found my purpose in life. I look back on the writing I did in school, and every chance I got I wrote about how it made no sense for us to eat animals.

Why would we kill another living being when we can easily live without causing its suffering?

I simply couldn't understand how anyone could love their dog and then turn around and eat a pig.

I saw all creatures on this earth as equal in their right to live. And I saw us, humans, as the only animals who have the ability to consciously choose whether or not we eat other animals.

Now, these strong beliefs came with a price, especially as I started getting older and started researching the truth about animal agriculture. What I discovered was so much worse than the image of Daniel Boone shooting Bambi.

The undercover photos and videos of animals in factory farms felt like a knife in my gut. I could feel the suffering of the animals, and it tore me apart.

When I understood the cruelty in the dairy and egg industries, I immediately went vegan.

I was 15.

Now, in my young mind, knowing it was my mission to save animals, I thought that if only people knew what was going on behind the closed doors of factory farms, then surely they would go vegan like I did!

I didn't see myself as different. I just thought I had discovered something other people weren't aware of yet.

So, I began my mission.

I was a leader in a local animal rights group, organizing protests before I could drive. I would leaflet every chance I got. I sat in cages on the sidewalk demonstrating the cramped conditions of chickens. I wore buttons on my shirt at school, asking people to boycott companies that tested on animals.

After a while, I came to understand that many people simply did not want to know the truth.

FOOD HEALS

This was a tough realization.

It was bigger than realizing that most people were not open to going vegan. It was the understanding that I was in a tiny, little minority of people who saw things as I did.

But that certainly didn't stop me. There's not a moment that I didn't know I'd be fighting for animals until the day I die.

I would call the vast majority of my adult life a period of life-experimentation and self-exploration. I experienced a lot of joy and excitement, but also dealt with a lot of shame and frustration.

I did some crazy things and was involved with some crazy people.

I feel like I've really lived and had experiences that, although I would never wish them on anyone else, I wouldn't take back even the most painful parts of that chapter in my life though. Every experience gave me an opportunity to learn and grow.

I see now just how resilient I am. And how cool is it that we can rewrite the stories we tell about who we are? It is amazing that we are that powerful!

Let me explain.

It started with my first serious boyfriend. He was an alcoholic and a drug addict. I was 18 and had just started college. One of the most memorable nights of my life was unfortunately a night of horror when he went on a drunken rampage. I think it was on that night that I wrote my story about being "unworthy" and "not good enough."

From there my self-image went downhill.

Beyond my mission of fighting for animal rights, I felt like I really didn't matter.

For the next 15 years I worked in the fitness industry and struggled with a distorted body image, disordered eating, depression, anxiety, and terrible insomnia.

But I struggled behind closed doors, in secret.

Women were amazed by my strong, lean body and I was a walking billboard against the negative stereotypes of what a vegan must look like. I inspired more people to start the transition to plant-based just by keeping myself in tip top shape than by anything else I could say or do.

I put a ton of pressure on myself to be a shining example of a healthy, fit, vegan. This meant I couldn't share any of my struggles.

People looked for reasons to challenge the vegan lifestyle, and I thought if I showed weakness, I would be giving them ammunition.

This contributed to the development of disordered eating patterns. I would restrict my food intake, count calories, track macros, and walk around hungry 95% of the time. The other 5%, I was binging, alone.

I remember eating an entire jar of peanut butter on multiple occasions.

The pressure I put on myself also led to body dysmorphia. I saw and felt fat that wasn't there. After a devastating breakup with my fiancé, I remember challenging myself to see if I could get below 100 pounds.

I'm not one to lose a challenge and I managed it. I'm 5'7."

My own food intake and weight were something I had control over. And with so much else out of my control, that gave me comfort.

It wasn't until 2016, many years after I had built a name for myself with my brand Sexy Fit Vegan, that I made it my mission to change my story of being unworthy and not good enough.

It was time to heal myself.

I self-coached my way to self-love. And the last piece of that involved ridding myself of the shame by getting vulnerable and sharing my story with the world, which I did in 2017.

It started with a series of blog posts called, "My Journey from Disordered Eating to Plant-Empowered Living."

Out of sharing came a sense of empowerment like I'd never experienced before.

I finally felt free in my authenticity.

The negative self-talk didn't just disappear all of a sudden, however. It's a process. It's a part of my journey that will take years and years to master, if ever.

I still observe self-destructive thoughts creeping in about my body and myself. I still get the urge to isolate myself and binge on vegan junk food at times when I feel down.

The difference is that I no longer let my feelings take my power away.

I am no longer a victim or my own worst enemy.

I started approaching myself with curiosity and compassion. I became confident in observing the defeating thoughts when they came up, while introducing thoughts that align with my new story of worthiness and self-love and acting on those healthy thoughts instead.

From there, I developed a whole new coaching program to serve people who not only have the desire to transition to a healthy vegan lifestyle, but who are also struggling with shame, an unhealthy relationship with food, a negative view of their bodies, and self-sabotaging behaviors.

The new program is based on true transformation through empowerment and self-love. It's built on the basis of aligning your actions with your values. It coaches people down the path toward not only a healthy and happy life, but also a free and meaningful life so they get to a place where they become an inspiration for others and make a positive impact in the world.

Although the program successfully helps people adopt a healthy, fit, and vegan lifestyle, the focus in not only about food!

Often, feeling powerless over food is just a symptom. And the countless diet plans and training programs they have been beating themselves up over just were attempts to put Band-aids on wounds that needed major surgery.

When we heal ourselves emotionally, physically, and spiritually, our lives can completely change.

My vegan diet is proof that food heals!

You can learn to love yourself, love your food, and love your body.

I did it and I know you can do it too!

And this leads me to where I am today, continuing to spread my message of veganism through empowerment, aligning your actions with your values, and rewriting your story with self-love as the foundation.

Ella Magers, MSW is the founder and CEO of Sexy Fit Vegan®. With 23 years as a vegan under her belt, Ella is a published author and speaker who has found extraordinary success empowering people to align their lifestyle with their values, create an empowered mindset, and build a healthy relationship with food, their bodies, and themselves.

Follow her work at SexyFitVegan.com.

Food Heals Podcast **Episodes 97, 170, 212, 217, 268 & 271**

CHAPTER 38 – MELISSA GLAZEWSKI: THAT DAMN SALISBURY STEAK

That Damn Salisbury Steak

By: Melissa Glazewski

Filed Under:
#foodheals #loveheals #thejourneyheals

It was March 21, 2018 in the afternoon when my phone rang. My mom was calling.

It's usually never a good sign when my mom wants to talk on the phone. The shaky voice on the other end said, "I'm at the hospital with Grandpa. He's not doing so well."

My heart immediately sank. My grandma had told her not to call me, but my mom knew I would want to talk with him one last time.

She handed the phone over, and my last conversation with him was mostly filled with morphine mumbles, although I did make out an "I love you." And I got to tell him how much I loved him and how I was going to get home to Wisconsin as soon as I could.

My grandpa passed away in the middle of the night on March 22.

Growing up, I spent so much time with my grandpa. He was like a second father to me. He was also my best friend and I loved hanging out with him.

He always had a joke to crack or a trick to play that would brighten everyone's day. He nicknamed me "Zooble" after the show Zoobilee Zoo (which I was obsessed with as a kid) and was the kind of guy who would make restaurant reservations under the name "Zooble" so that they'd have to call it out.

That always excited me, but it did become slightly embarrassing as I got older. Regardless, that nickname followed me into my 30s and is something I now cherish.

As a kid, I loved helping my grandma in the kitchen. And since I spent a lot of time at their house, it was something I did often.

FOOD HEALS

I would help mix the jell-o, bread the pork chops, scoop the cookie dough, peel the potatoes, and open the canned vegetables. We always ate together at her kitchen table, which I looked forward to since we didn't do that at home.

On rare occasions, my grandpa would eat at the table with us, but he mostly ate at his chair with his TV tray in the living room. I would proudly serve him his plate, glass of milk, and salt shaker.

At this age, you're not thinking about what you're eating or about the positive effects of eating together at a table versus in front of a TV. You just assume 'it's the way it is' and even good for you, since your family members allow it.

My grandpa lived off of frozen salisbury steak dinners and canned vegetables for years. Canned vegetables were the only ones he would touch, and for most of my life, I assumed they were healthy. I mean, they had to be if my grandma had 200+ cans of them in her basement, right?!

As I got older, and after going vegetarian at age 18, I began to realize that this food and way of living was not healthy at all. However, at that time I didn't realize just how detrimental processed foods were and was still eating vegan junk food regularly.

It took years for me to get educated on food, health, nutrition, and wellness. The more I learned, the more I shared with my family because I wanted them to live healthier lives too.

To this day, they still mainly eat the disease-causing Standard American Diet but have become receptive to healthier eating, which is a huge step in the right direction!

Knowing what I know now, I feel it is my duty to educate them. And when they develop a disease or their health fails them, I feel extreme guilt. Guilt because I should have helped them more.

I feel anger too. Anger that they wouldn't listen to me or do more.

And none of this hit me as hard as it did when my grandpa's disease took over. He had been sick for awhile. Always battling something, my grandpa was a strong man who kept powering through. Eventually though, he just became too weak.

My grandma made frequent, long drives to take him to doctor's appointments. It was exhausting — taking care of him, cleaning up after him, and dealing with his bad mood. She was doing everything she could for him and getting nowhere.

In February of 2018, it got to the point where I knew I had to visit and help. My grandparents had recently moved three hours north of the city where the rest of our family lives and were a bit isolated from us.

I spent two weeks with my grandparents, helping them with anything they needed and taking time to bond with them. I went into this visit with so many ideas of how I could help my grandpa. I had supplements he could take, I made an immune-boosting broth for all of us, I had a meditation we could do — mainly for my grandma to help relieve stress — and I really thought I could help him feel better.

My grandpa rarely went to doctors before this and would almost never listen to their advice, but he would often call me to get my advice and see what I would recommend, since I have a healthcare background. He often dubbed me as his "nurse," and it always made me smile.

There were still many times he didn't listen to me either, but the times he did made me feel like a champion. Even if he did call probiotics "yogurt pills," at least he was taking them!

Upon my arrival for those two weeks, I knew there wasn't much I could do. My grandpa was the sickest I had ever seen him and in great pain. The moans that came out of him every time he moved were unlike anything I had heard.

It was heart-wrenching to witness.

It felt like just yesterday was 2002 and we were playing tennis together in Hawaii, and now, here he was barely able to walk. He kept telling me, "I just want to get some strength back."

What do you say to someone when you know that it's not going to happen?

Watching your best friend struggle with their health for years, knowing the changes they could make to improve their health, but seeing them resistant to most of it? That's one of the most painful experiences.

And this is why I do what I do.

I refuse to keep losing people I love to preventable diseases. Whether or not people listen or take action is ultimately on them, but I need to know that I'm doing my part to help people live healthier lives.

It's as simple as this: With every bite we take, we're either preventing disease or causing it.

I don't want to blame all of those damn frozen salisbury steaks, but whenever I think back on my childhood, the image of a freezer filled to the brim with them is what I remember most about how my grandpa ate.

When I think back on my grandpa as a person, I see my best friend and a man who spent so many years making my life better with the joy he brought to it.

And although I feel guilt around not being able to keep him here longer, I know that I made his life better too and I can't wait to see him again.

In December 2017, Melissa Glazewski left her office job to pursue her passion for healthy living and cooking full-time, which led her to create her brand Forkin' Plants. She has a healthcare background, is a personal chef, and loves hosting events and demos to help educate people on how to live their best (plant-based!) life.

Follow her work at ForkinPlants.com.

Food Heals Podcast **Episodes 218, 250 & 254**

CHAPTER 39 – MAšA OFEI: LIVING LIFE WITH INTENTION

Living Life with Intention

By: Maša Ofei

Filed Under:
#foodheals #loveheals #thejourneyheals

In July 2013, something wonderful happened. My husband Michael stumbled across a blog called Zen Habits.

It was through this blog that he learned how to pursue *less* through minimalism, so we could create white space in our lives and ultimately do what we really wanted.

He introduced the concept of minimalism to me, and at first, I thought, "I don't like the sound of living in a white house, with white walls and white furniture."

However, once I truly understood what minimalism was, we were well on our path to minimizing our possessions and freeing ourselves from what we call "The More Virus."

You see, up until this time in our lives, Michael and I were caught in the "busy being busy race" — always thinking that the grass was greener on the other side.

Michael was in real estate and defined success by having more. More sales, more money, more houses, more security. That's just how the industry works. But working 12-hour days and taking calls at all hours of the night was not a life I wanted to be a part of.

So with that, I gave him an ultimatum. I knew how much he loved his career, but I didn't see myself in that world. Michael made the tough decision to leave real estate and pursue a path of personal growth without compromising quality time with me.

At that time, I was also wrapping up my photography business that was no longer bringing me joy, and that's when things started to align. The question of what we really wanted to achieve and get out of life was sitting right there, waiting for us to address it.

We took a long hard look at ourselves and made some tough and confronting decisions.

I remember clearing out boxes of papers simply by scanning them. Oh, what a liberating feeling that was! Looking at everything that we owned, we carefully considered if it really had a purpose in our lives. It certainly helped that we moved three times in two years, so each time we got rid of more stuff. By the third move, we had probably donated, sold, or gifted half of what we had.

Learning about minimalism opened up my eyes in ways I honestly didn't think was possible. Minimalism taught me how to question the status quo and how to be confident in defining success for both of us, not based on what others thought.

This was a massive step and realization.

As I was (and to an extent still am) a people-pleaser, I wanted to make sure that I never hurt anyone's feelings. Sometimes though, I've realized that it's okay to be a little more selfish and look out for yourself.

In this time, we also addressed more than just possessions. I had no idea that minimalism was so much more than just decluttering. We spent less time with people who didn't make us happy and we re-evaluated all of our commitments.

Minimalism gave us an entirely new outlook on life.

It genuinely made us happier.

Six months into the minimalism journey, Michael decided to spring something else on me. One day, I remember it quite clearly, I was sitting at my desk and received an email from Michael saying, "Want to watch this tonight?"

It was a YouTube preview to the documentary *Earthlings*. I watched the short clip and was horrified, quickly responding, "No thanks!"

Something came over me though. I guess I was intrigued, and the curiosity that I naturally have in me to know the truth made me come home and say, "You know what? Okay, let's watch it!"

After two hours passed with many breaks and tears along the way, we finished it.

The documentary took us on a journey of how humans exploit animals in agriculture, entertainment, animal testing, domestic breeding, and fashion. This is the moment we both became vegan.

That was in August of 2014.

After first becoming minimalists and then later vegans, we decided that we wanted to start a meaningful project together. I had been talking about working with Michael on something for years, but it never felt quite right. Something that was completely ours. That we built from the ground up and that we connected on deeply.

We finally found the perfect topics. Those two things were minimalism and veganism. The underlying theme that links the two values together is conscious consumerism, which is something I've been fascinated by for a while.

Living with intentionality became our mission in life.

As the years went on, I became slightly obsessed with natural health and making sure that I shared what I learned with others through recipes and in some of the content I wrote for our blog.

Not only was I loving learning the benefits of being a vegan, but also saw the freedom that minimalism had created in my life. For someone who has suffered from stress and anxiety for a long time, I found minimalism to be the perfect antidote to a lot of the issues I had in the past.

When I started seeking less and not caring as much about what others thought of me, it made getting through each day much clearer. I felt surer in myself because of the values that I have in my life and how strongly I feel about them. No one could rock that or make me question whether what I was doing was right or wrong.

With the passion that I had for health and sharing products that I found along the way, I struggled to find a store where I could get my everyday essentials — yes, even minimalists still buy products.

I often had to shop at multiple health food stores or online niche shops to get simple items like shampoo and toothpaste because my standards were so high. I've always been puzzled why nobody else seemed to care as much as I did.

So instead of waiting for a solution to come along, I decided to solve my own problem and started an online store called Fairlings. Along with Michael, our goal was to make shopping for organic, vegan, ethical, and sustainable products more accessible and the best we could find based on rigorous research.

Since we're minimalists, we also implemented another polarizing idea of how to do retail. We only stocked one brand per product category.

Ultimately, this project was about shifting the demand for ethical products in the marketplace and encouraging mindful consumerism.

Starting an online store was a massive undertaking for us, and that anxiety and stress began to creep back in again. Fairlings ended up taking priority over The Minimalist Vegan, which made me feel a little uneasy inside.

After two years of running the online store and growing the range, we decided to call it quits.

The thought of spreading ourselves so thin and stocking a warehouse full of things made me start to question if that's what I really wanted. The answer was plain and simple, no.

This was a pretty scary realization because we had worked so hard to build it up and had the most amazing, loyal customers. The only thing was that I felt that there was more to life than selling ethical, organic everyday essentials. I was pulled back to our blog, to give that more attention. To write more, to read more, to create more.

After publishing our first book at the start of 2018, we receive feedback all the time on how our writing has changed people's lives. That's something that I wanted to pursue.

One thing that I've always done is be true to myself. I look at how something sits within me and how I see it unfolding in the future, and if there's hesitation or doubt, I know to address it. I've always been certain that life is too short to be doing things I don't want to be doing.

I wasn't scared to close my successful photography business after studying photography for over five years and running a business for four years.

I wasn't afraid to take the time to find myself again and do jobs that I enjoyed even though a kid still in high school could be doing it too.

I would pick this lifestyle over being stuck in a job I hate every single time. My brain is not wired that way, and I'm grateful for that.

I wanted to get back to basics. To create from the heart and give myself permission to sit down and read a book in the middle of the day without having my to-do list make me feel a cloud of guilt.

Michael and I both love the idea of minimalist blogging, which is the process of creating a body of work that we're genuinely proud of. Something that's pure and unique to how we see the world, not because it's going to go viral.

I've learned that everything happens for a reason, and I am where I am today because of everything that has happened to me in the past.

I wouldn't change any of it.

Maša Ofei is the co-founder of The Minimalist Vegan, a blog on how to live with less stuff and more compassion. She's a health coach and professional photographer.

Her favorite things are going to farmers markets and spending time with her husband and fur baby.

Follow her work at TheMinimalistVegan.com.

***Food Heals Podcast* Episode 221**

CHAPTER 40 – TARASHAUN HAUSNER: HOW A POPULAR KITCHEN APPLIANCE HELPED ME HEAL, GET HEALTHY, AND LOVE MY BODY

How a Popular Kitchen Appliance Helped Me Heal, Get Healthy, and Love My Body

By: Tarashaun Hausner

Filed Under:
#foodheals #spiritheals #thejourneyheals

"What is this?" my boyfriend asked as he pointed to a cup of food I had placed in the trash earlier.

I searched for an answer but didn't have one that would justify what he found.

He continued rifling through the garbage and found several more of the meals I'd chewed up and spewed into cups that I tried to hide in the trash.

It never dawned on me that he (or anyone for that matter) would ever find out. I had successfully kept my "habit" under wraps for more than 10 years.

Suddenly, things were unfolding fast and there was nothing I could do or say to keep from having to face the truth — I had bulimia.

The look of disgust on my boyfriend's face at what he found in the trash mirrored how I felt about myself.

Like others who struggle with bulimia, I started binging and purging in secrecy.

As the years passed and my teeth and gums began to show signs of damage, I transitioned to binge chewing. I put all the unswallowed food into cups that I would later bury in the trash.

Unable to truly explain to my boyfriend why, that night I swore to him and myself that I would get some much-needed help.

TARASHAUN HAUSNER

My struggle with bulimia was a byproduct of so many things happening in my life and my inability to cope with any of it.

At the root of it all was the belief I was ugly and unworthy of love.

Also, my mother had been diagnosed with bi-polar disorder and I, too, struggled with depression.

I self-medicated with food — lots of it.

The meals I ate, I later purged. Everything else was covertly chewed and spewed.

I started seeing a therapist. Unfortunately, after a few sessions she told me she couldn't help me and suggested I find someone more familiar with my disorder.

I was crushed and didn't want to go through the process again of finding someone to talk to about the disorder, so I resolved to handle it on my own.

I started by reading as many self-help and spiritual books as I could get my hands on.

All of the reading I did made me feel like change was possible. I was doing well.

And then my boyfriend and I broke up.

I was afraid of being alone but wanted to keep striving to get better. I'd gotten a new apartment and a new job. I also started a meditation practice that helped me with my feelings of anxiety.

During one incredibly stressful and lonely moment, I binge ate as much food as I could possibly fit into my body and then purged. I cried for hours and felt myself sinking back into old thought patterns of shame, disgust, and unworthiness.

A voice in my head reminded me that I had come a long way (on my own, no less) and I needed to find the courage to forgive myself so I could continue on with my journey.

And that night I made a decision. It's a decision that I have upheld ever since.

FOOD HEALS

I said, "NO MORE."

I've often heard people say you can do anything if you put your mind to it, but it never meant anything until it became real for me.

There really is something amazing about the impact willpower can have on your life when you feel that's all you have to get you through each day.

So I continued my reading and learning everything about how to eat healthy. I focused a lot of time on revamping my eating habits.

I added more whole foods to my daily meals. These foods nourished my body and mind, and they made me feel good.

Almost every health "guru" I had come across in my on-going quest for information on how to eat and live better was a strong proponent of juicing.

I loved the idea of making fresh fruit and vegetable juices, so I decided to purchase a juicer. I ended up finding something else that would turn my life around personally and professionally.

While shopping for a juicer at my local warehouse store, I watched a demonstration for a high-powered blender by Blendtec. I was truly amazed at the power and functionality of this seemingly standard looking blender. I stood there for what seemed like hours watching the Blendtec rep make a variety of things in the blender.

A delicious soup was first. The idea that a steaming hot soup could be poured from the blender jar without needing to heat it on the stove blew my mind!

A green juice was next. There was no need for cutting, peeling, or deseeding. Everything was put in the blender and it liquefied it all — the fiber, seeds, skin, and all.

I later found out that this kind of juice was much healthier and more cost efficient than those made from regular juice extractors.

My mind was blown again when the blender rep prepared a yummy ice cream that had cabbage of all things in it.

I was amazed at all the many things a high-powered blender could make.

So, I scrapped my plan of buying a juicer and purchased a blender instead. It was the best decision I'd made in my life.

Not only did it help me stay committed to living healthier, but it also became a de facto career.

Shortly after purchasing the blender I, too, became a Blendtec roadshow demonstrator in California. It was my job to show prospective buyers how and why owning a high-powered blender would help them achieve their health goals.

I was the perfect person to share this information because blending gave me a new perspective on how to eat and prepare healthy food.

Though traveling around California was fun, I wanted to reach more people and there was no better way to do it than with the internet.

When I wasn't on the road, I was busy developing a website and blog that would enable me to share everything I knew about blenders and healthy eating and living — without having to travel.

I launched BlenderBabes.com in 2013.

Initially, I was concerned no one would take me seriously because I wasn't like some of the other health "experts." I am not a doctor. I'm also not a holistic nutritionist...yet.

I am merely a regular person who has struggled with low self-esteem and a poor body image that led to an eating disorder and depression.

But I was able to change my life significantly in a bit of an unconventional way.

Buying my first power blender and using it every day became the game-changer for me and I haven't looked back.

Healthy, whole-food-based recipes (many which I had created myself) and how-to videos became the staple for Blender Babes. Then I realized I could do much more than just be a "food blogger."

I still created recipes and how-to videos, but I focused more energy on making Blender Babes into a community for people who wanted to change their diets and their minds about how they viewed food and their bodies.

Having struggled with a poor body image and low self-esteem for so many years, I took a bold step and shared my story. I also stepped out of my comfort zone and donned a bikini in several of the how-to videos I filmed for the site.

My goal was to show that the Blender Babes consisted of women of all nationalities and life experiences who had real bodies that were curvaceous and looked healthy as opposed to "model thin."

Although I received some negative feedback about the Blender Babes wearing swimwear, I didn't allow the disapproving response to influence how I felt about myself or overshadow my primary objective of living a healthier lifestyle and helping others learn how to do the same.

Since starting Blender Babes, I have helped over 10,000 people buy blenders (as I write this in early 2019).

I am now on a mission to reach 1 million people.

In addition to providing detailed information on what to look for and how to purchase a good high-powered blender, I am also creating programs to help my community.

For example, with a nutritionist, I developed a 7-day whole foods Blender Cleanse™ that helps detox and nourish the body. I'll be releasing a new clean eating and blending meal plan program as well.

I know what it's like to feel lost and alone. I know what it's like to struggle with physical and mental health issues.

I never imagined a kitchen appliance would become my saving grace. But it has. I have not had a bulimic episode in over eight years.

Using my blender to eat more whole-foods-based meals has changed how I eat, prepare, and view food.

I guess you can say what helped me heal has also become the motto for my business: "Live Healthier. Get a Blender."

Tarashaun Hausner is the founder of Blender Babes. She credits using a blender daily for helping her heal an unhealthy relationship with food.

A passionate advocate for healthy living, she is committed to helping others pursue optimal wellness and heal their bodies with clean eating.

Learn more at BlenderBabes.com.

Food Heals Podcast Episode 145

CHAPTER 41 – LAUREN TATARCHUK: WHAT I'VE LEARNED ON MY HEALING JOURNEY

What I've Learned on My Healing Journey

By: Lauren Tatarchuk

Filed Under:
#foodheals #loveheals #alternativemedicineheals

From the age of 12, I was a "medical mystery."

Diagnoses proclaimed: fibromyalgia, chronic fatigue, lupus, Lyme disease.

I struggled with chronic pain, exhaustion, muscle weakness, severe migraines, and so much more.

I didn't even have the strength to get through the day without 80mg of Adderall.

I was so heavily medicated that I don't remember much of my adolescence. I took a shoebox of pills every day — until one day I snapped, ripped the medicine cabinet off the wall, and threw the pills across the room.

I fell to the floor, sobbing. Enough was enough.

I had lived my whole life in limbo, somewhere between not being sick enough that I was dying but not being well enough that I was living. I didn't want to manage my suffering anymore, I wanted to *heal*.

Enough with the pills and enough with the victim mentality. I'd had enough of the medical crutches. I was going to let my pain fuel my motivation to get well naturally.

I didn't know how I'd do it, but a voice from within whispered that it was possible.

From that day on, I started using myself as a guinea pig. Through a combination of changing my diet, going vegan, getting off the pills, working on my subconscious mind, healing old emotional wounds, and adding a plethora of alternative healing modalities to my routine, I did it.

I healed myself.

It really was a marathon, not a sprint.

Slow and steady, day-by-day, that's how healing happens — *gradually* and *in its own time*.

At some point during my healing journey, I became aware of one major thing that was holding me back: I kept waiting to live my life until "later," when I was "better" and "100% healed."

I realized that healing could only truly begin when I remembered to live, *while* I was healing, and to love myself *even if* I am hurting.

Only when I started to do that did everything finally come together.

Having healed myself of debilitating conditions, I now know what is possible and want to be a message of hope to anyone suffering with chronic illness.

To those suffering: You are not your symptoms, diagnoses, struggles, or traumas.

You are the beautiful being beyond all those things. You are the one rising above it, using it to fuel your inner growth, healing, and rebirth to become the best, most powerful version of yourself.

For the first time in my life, I'm learning who I am without sickness. Surprisingly, I think that has been the scariest part of the whole healing journey.

I had been sick my whole life, who would I be without it?

This part of the journey happens gradually also. Everyday I learn more and more about the person inside of this physical body and what she's here to do.

I'm feeling like *Lauren-Unleashed* and it's exciting, scary, and beautiful all at once. And I wouldn't have it any other way.

Here are the foundational truths that I have learned throughout this healing journey:

• I've learned I have to be what I'm looking for.

• I've learned that doing things "in spite of" or "in fear of" will never result in anything but suffering.

• I've learned to move forward from and with my intention — a.k.a. my heart.

• I've learned I can have anything I'm willing to work for.

• I've learned it's best to forget everything everyone's ever told me about what I should or shouldn't do or what's possible and impossible.

• I've learned all it takes is concentrated action interlaced with focus, discipline, commitment, grit, persistence, passion, and a burning desire and belief to make it come about.

• I've learned to work harder on myself than anything else in life.

• I've learned how to move from being the victim to being the one in charge.

• I've learned not everyone wants to hear what I've learned.

• I've learned some people will not like when I change, but it's okay because only I have to like me.

• I've learned other people's reactions towards me have absolutely nothing to do with me and that what other people think about me is none of my business.

• I've learned I don't have to explain myself to anyone, no matter who they are.

• I've learned that when I'm stuck, I must try and see what I'm not considering that's otherwise obvious.

• I've learned that the word '*psyche*' is derived from a Greek word that means '*soul.*'

FOOD HEALS

- I've learned the more I resist, the more things persist. If I stop resisting and forcing, and just do me — just be me — I will be led forward.

- I've learned all I really need in life is wisdom and awareness because I can get everything else from there.

- I've learned that change is the only constant.

- I've learned that if something is true, it is true on all levels.

- I've learned I can feel uncomfortable and be in pain physically but at the same time be truly happy on the inside.

- I've learned the most important thing I can learn in life is who I really am, what makes me tick, and what gets my motors churning — and then be it.

- I've learned to lick the spoon joyfully, with pleasure, not with guilt (damnit!).

- I've learned that no matter what I do or what happens, I can always win, because I can always choose to learn something.

- I've learned that I must lean into my fears and uncomfortable feelings to pass through them and come out on the other side liberated and free.

- I've learned that "to really live" means to be free from myself, because I am the one holding myself back.

- I've learned that this whole crazy thing called life is for me to catch up to myself; I already have the potential, I just have to take concentrated action to get there.

- I've learned that I don't have to be perfect, I just have to be okay when things aren't exactly the way that I'd like them to be.

- I've learned that fear is the point-of-impact where all suffering stems from and that there is nothing to fear but fear itself.

- I've learned that instead of trying to resonate with outside, external factors, I must find my resonance within.

LAUREN TATARCHUK

- I've learned that my wounds are my wisdom and that showing up is the first step.

- I've learned that for anything to come into fruition, I just have to start and take one step. Then each subsequent step will be revealed to me.

- I've learned that what I lack in natural ability, I can make up for in self-discipline, love, focus, commitment, compassion, courage, and asking for help.

- I've learned that my life "degree" or life "cred" is far more important than any degree or certification I can ever get from a university, institute, or program.

- I've learned to say yes to learning, growing, and serving.

- I've learned that both conscious and unconscious emotions, perceptions, and mental attitudes play a role in all aspects of health, dis-ease, overall well-being, and quality of life.

- I've learned I must give my all and then detach from the outcome.

- I've learned to say "no" in a big way and "yes" in an even bigger way.

- I've learned that life is meant to be enjoyed, not to be a constant struggle.

- I've learned that if I'm not enjoying life, I can change the direction of it at any second with a single pivot.

- I've learned I can either get bitter or get better in any and every situation.

- I've learned the most important things that make up my life are those that I cannot see like love, will, grit, passion, my immune system, oxygen, and my connection to something bigger than myself.

- I've learned I am not here to do things for others, but rather empower and teach them to do it for themselves.

- I've learned that no one is me, and that is my power.

FOOD HEALS

- I've learned to stop waiting to love myself until "later" when things are different and start loving myself right now, as I am and as situations are.

- I've learned that this too shall pass and that thoughts become things.

- I've learned that if I want green grass — just water it for goodness sake.

- I've learned that nothing ever goes away until it has taught me what I need to know.

- I've learned I must be stronger than my fears and much, much wiser.

- I've learned it takes courage to take care of myself the way I know I need to.

- I've learned that the strongest of us tend to be hurting the most.

- I've learned that it's okay to rest when I'm tired.

- I've learned that healing is far more than the physical body, it's the emotional, spiritual, and mental well-being all interlaced.

- I've learned the only way "to" is "through" and that when I want to give up is exactly when I must find the strength to continue on.

- I've learned that the old must deteriorate for the new to arise.

- I've learned to feel like I've never felt, I must do what I've never done.

- I've learned that if I can be disciplined enough and willing to heal myself, I can do absolutely anything else in life.

- I've learned healing is not for the faint of heart and that if I want it badly enough, I'll do it.

- I've learned it doesn't matter how hard or painful healing and change is, staying where I am is even harder.

- I've learned that when I feel like my body is punishing me, it's not, it's simply the messenger. And I've learned to thank the messenger and listen to it instead of being mad at it and suppressing or ignoring it.

• I've learned the hard way that it gets worse before it gets better and, no matter what, I must continue forward with steadfast virtue.

• I've learned there's absolutely no quick fix. The only way out is the way I came in.

• I've learned the road less traveled is the path of least resistance.

• I've learned when I find myself in the majority, it's time to run the other way — fast.

• I've learned I'm so much stronger than I can fathom, even when — no, especially when — I feel like the total opposite.

• I've learned it's the easiest thing in the world to quit and that it's the hardest thing to push through, over and over and over again.

• I've learned it's okay to feel whatever it is I'm feeling.

• I've learned to love others enough to let them have their own journey.

• I've learned to give advice only when asked (kind of).

• I've learned my body is always working for me, even when it doesn't feel that way.

• I've learned to love myself even when it hurts to be loving and when the struggle is real.

• I've learned long-term sustainability over short-term pleasure mentality.

• I've learned that I'm beautiful even when I can't look at myself in the mirror because I just don't recognize the face and physical body looking back at me.

• I've learned it's okay to be me, to take care of myself, and to stand up for what I believe.

• I've learned that only I can heal myself.

• I've learned to trust my body and the process one more time, and always one more time.

• I've learned that healing is extremely volatile and beautiful and guess what? It's always worth it.

• I've learned the whole point of our existence is the quality of our life experience.

It all starts on the inside, in our hearts, in ourselves — our awareness to see change is necessary, our wisdom to realize that only we can do it, and our willingness to take the first step — that's what it's all about.

Lauren Tatarchuk has been on a crazy, wild journey to heal herself. She has overcome pharmaceutical addiction and dependency, debilitating physical symptoms, and crippling emotional and mental obstacles. She is here to inspire others into action and share what she's learned.

Follow along at Instagram.com/WhatIveLearnedNotes.

Food Heals Podcast **Episode 158**